READER'S GUIDE

AND ACTIVITY WORKBOOK

Units 1–12

EMC/Paradigm Publishing
St. Paul, Minnesota

Staff Credits:

For **EMC/Paradigm Publishing,** St. Paul, Minnesota

Laurie Skiba
Editor

Eileen Slater
Editorial Consultant

Shannon O'Donnell Taylor
Associate Editor

Jennifer J. Anderson
Assistant Editor

For **Penobscot School Publishing, Inc.,** Danvers, Massachusetts

Editorial

Robert D. Shepherd
President, Executive Editor

Christina E. Kolb
Managing Editor

Kim Leahy Beaudet
Editor

Sara Hyry
Editor

Laurie A. Faria
Associate Editor

Sharon Salinger
Copyeditor

Marilyn Murphy Shepherd
Editorial Advisor

Design and Production

Charles Q. Bent
Production Manager

Sara Day
Art Director

Diane Castro
Compositor

Janet Stebbings
Compositor

ISBN 0-8219-1566-5

© 1998 by EMC Corporation

Published by EMC/Paradigm Publishing
875 Montreal Way
St. Paul, Minnesota 55102

Printed in the United States of America
10 9 8 7 6 5 4 3 2 1 xxx 03 02 01 00 99 98

Contents

Unit 8

Unit 9

Unit 10

Unit 11

Unit 12

Selection Worksheet

from *Like Water for Chocolate*, page 9

READER RESPONSE ACTIVITIES

1. **Reader's Journal, page 10.** What traditions does your family practice? Describe one tradition that you would like to pass on to the family you may create one day and explain why. Describe a tradition you don't want to pass on to your future family, and explain why not.

   _____

   _____

   _____

   _____

   _____

   _____

   _____

   _____

   _____

   _____

   _____

   _____

   _____

   _____

   _____

   _____

   _____

   _____

   _____

2. **Guided Reading.** Answer these questions as you read the selection.

   Page 10: Where does Tita make her entrance into the world?

   _____

   _____

   Page 10: How does Tita enter the world?

   _____

   _____

Page 10: What effect does Tita's unusual birth have on her life?

_____

_____

Page 11: Who offers to take charge of Tita's feeding? In what is this person an expert?

_____

_____

Page 11: What do Tita's sisters think of playing in the kitchen?

_____

_____

Page 11: How does Tita feel about laughter and sorrow?

_____

_____

Page 11: Because Tita's life is so wrapped up in the kitchen, what is difficult for her to comprehend?

_____

_____

Page 12: What are the ingredients that are listed at the beginning of this selection used to make? Who loves this recipe?

_____

_____

Page 12: What power does Tita believe that smells have?

_____

_____

Page 13: What is not permitted in the household? What does Mama Elena do to enforce this rule?

_____

_____

Page 13: What does Tita do when she learns her fate? What does she realize? What does the table "realize"?

_____

_____

Page 13: Who wants to come and speak with Mama Elena?

_____

_____

Page 13: What has "flowed over the family"?

_____

_____

Page 13: In Mama Elena's family, what does being the youngest daughter mean for Tita?

_____

_____

Page 14: Why do Pedro Muzquiz and his father appear at the house?

_____

_____

Page 14: What did Tita ask Pedro to do?

_____

_____

Page 15: Whom does Mama Elena suggest that Pedro marry?

_____

_____

Page 15: How does Tita feel about Pedro's decision to marry Rosaura? How do you think she felt about Pedro?

_____

_____

Page 15: What is Pedro's reason for agreeing to marry Rosaura?

_____

_____

Page 15: To what does Chencha compare Mama Elena's proposal?

_____

_____

Page 15: What does Pedro say about his love for Tita?

_____

_____

3. **Responding to the Selection, page 16.** How do you feel about Pedro's decision to marry Tita's sister Rosaura? Do you think his decision can be justified using his reasoning? Explain your opinion about Pedro's decision on the lines below.

_____

_____

_____

_____

_____

_____

_____

_____

_____

_____

_____

_____

_____

_____

_____

_____

_____

_____

_____

_____

_____

_____

_____

_____

_____

_____

_____

_____

Selection Worksheet

1.2

"Marriage Is a Private Affair," page 24

READER RESPONSE ACTIVITIES

1. **Reader's Journal, page 25.** For thousands of years, in most cultures around the globe, marriages were arranged by parents. Husbands and wives were chosen based on social position, wealth, family reputation, and other such criteria. Why do modern men and women typically object to arranged marriages? What might be positive aspects of arranged marriages? negative aspects? How do reasons for marrying in the modern age differ from reasons for marrying in the past? Respond to these questions on the lines below.

_____

_____

_____

_____

_____

_____

_____

_____

_____

_____

_____

2. **Guided Reading.** Answer these questions as you read the selection.

    Page 25: Why is Nnaemeka worried about telling his father about his engagement?

    _____

    _____

    Page 26: Why does Nnaemeka say that he cannot marry Ugoye?

    _____

    _____

    Page 26: What does Nnaemeka's father think about marrying for love? What qualities does he believe make a good wife?

    _____

    _____

Page 27: What has Nnaemeka's father decided to do?

_____

_____

Page 28: What makes Nnaemeka's decision particularly shocking to the villagers?

_____

_____

Page 28: What does Okeke do to his son's wedding picture? Why? How does Nene feel about her father-in-law's reaction?

_____

_____

Page 28: What is Okeke's attitude toward his son?

_____

_____

Page 29: Over time how do people's attitudes change toward Nene?

_____

_____

Page 29: What has Okeke won? What has he lost?

_____

_____

Page 29: What does Nene ask of her father-in-law?

_____

_____

3. **Responding to the Selection, page 30.** Do you agree with the beliefs and actions of Nnaemeka's father at the beginning of the story? in the middle? at the very end? Do you disagree with him? Do you feel understanding or compassion for him? What lesson do you think he has learned by the end of the story?

_____

_____

_____

_____

_____

_____

Selection Worksheet

1.3

"Poseidonians," page 37

READER RESPONSE ACTIVITIES

1. **Reader's Journal, page 38.** What do you know about the ancestry of your family? What interests you the most when you think about your ancestors? If you don't have specific information, try to imagine details about your ancestors based on what you know of particular countries or time periods. Write your thoughts about your ancestors on the lines below.

   _____

   _____

   _____

   _____

   _____

   _____

   _____

   _____

   _____

   _____

   _____

2. **Guided Reading.** Answer these questions as you read the selection.

   Page 38: What have the Poseidonians forgotten? What is the only ancestral thing that remains to them?

   _____

   _____

   Page 38: What do the Poseidonians do toward the festival's end?

   _____

   _____

   Page 38: Why does the festival always have a melancholy ending? How is the Poseidonian way of living and speaking described?

   _____

   _____

3. **Responding to the Selection, page 39.** Today many people feel depressed after the excitement of a major holiday. Why do you think this is so? In what way is this reaction similar to or different from the "melancholy ending" to the Poseidonians' Greek festival?

_____

_____

_____

_____

_____

_____

_____

_____

_____

_____

_____

_____

_____

_____

_____

_____

_____

_____

_____

_____

_____

_____

_____

_____

_____

_____

_____

Selection Worksheet

1.4

from *The Bald Soprano*, page 46

READER RESPONSE ACTIVITIES

1. **Reader's Journal, page 47.** What aspects of human nature and society, our habits, traditions, and social customs, do you find absurd? Why do these aspects of human nature or society seem particularly absurd or nonsensical to you? On the lines below, describe something that makes no sense to you.

_____

_____

_____

_____

_____

_____

_____

_____

_____

_____

2. **Guided Reading.** Answer these questions as you read the selection.

   Page 47: Where do Mr. Martin and Mrs. Martin believe they might have previously seen each other? What does Mrs. Martin say she lacks?

   _____

   _____

   Page 47: When did both characters leave Manchester?

   _____

   _____

   Page 48: What do the Martins discover about their train trip?

   _____

   _____

   Page 48: Why is Mrs. Martin surprised when Mr. Martin describes where he lives?

   _____

   _____

Page 48: What does Mr. Martin remember about Mrs. Martin?

_____

_____

Page 49: What is unusual about the clock?

_____

_____

Page 49: What characteristics do Mrs. Martin's daughter and Mr. Martin's daughter share?

_____

_____

Page 50: What conclusion does Mr. Martin reach concerning Mrs. Martin?

_____

_____

Page 50: What does Mary tell the audience about the Martins? What is the reasoning behind her statement?

_____

_____

Page 50: What questions does Mary ask? What does she claim is her real name?

_____

_____

3. **Responding to the Selection, page 50.** Imagine that you overheard the conversation between Mr. Martin and Mrs. Martin. Would you interrupt them at any point to clue them in about their relationship? If so, what would you say? Based on the conversation you overheard, how would you describe the Martins to your friends?

_____

_____

_____

_____

_____

_____

_____

_____

Selection Worksheet

"Conversation with an American Writer," page 58

READER RESPONSE ACTIVITIES

1. **Reader's Journal, page 59.** What is an honest person? Do you consider yourself to be honest? Have you ever been in a situation in which you were afraid to tell the truth? Do you feel that you made the right decision? On the lines below, record your views about honesty and dishonesty and describe an occasion when you were torn as to whether you should tell the truth.

_____

_____

_____

_____

_____

_____

_____

_____

_____

_____

_____

_____

2. **Guided Reading.** Answer these questions as you read the selection.

Page 59: Does the speaker consider himself "fearless"? What does the speaker consider it unworthy to do?

_____

_____

Page 59: At what has the speaker laughed?

_____

_____

Page 59: In what way does the speaker describe his writing?

_____

_____

Page 59: Why did the speaker distinguish the "talented" from the "incapable" in his writing?

_____

_____

Page 60: What will our descendants remember?

_____

_____

3. **Responding to the Selection, page 61.** List examples of how the speaker, as an honest critic, might evaluate current American life in such arenas as politics, the economy, social issues, the media, or the environment.

_____

_____

_____

_____

_____

_____

_____

_____

_____

_____

_____

_____

_____

_____

_____

_____

_____

_____

_____

_____

Selection Worksheet

1.6

from *Nectar in a Sieve*, page 69

READER RESPONSE ACTIVITIES

1. **Reader's Journal, page 70.** What are some of the advantages of living in a busy town that attracts large businesses and new people? What are some of the advantages of living in a small village, in which people know one another and small businesses thrive? What would it be like to have to move from one to the other? On the lines below, write about what you would need to do to adapt.

_____

_____

_____

_____

_____

_____

_____

_____

_____

_____

_____

_____

_____

_____

_____

_____

2. **Guided Reading.** Answer these questions as you read the selection.

   Page 70: Why does Kunthi find the tannery to be a "boon"?

   _____

   _____

   Page 70: Does the narrator prefer the quiet village life of the past or the growing town in which she now lives? What changes has she noticed in her town?

   _____

   _____

Page 71: What happens to the small shop as a result of the new tannery in town? Why are other shopkeepers glad?

_____

_____

Page 72: What kinds of people are officials at the tannery? Where do some of them live?

_____

_____

Page 72: What talk does Kali's husband feel is useless? Why does he feel this way?

_____

_____

Page 72: Why does the narrator feel sorry for the wives of the Muslim officials? Why doesn't the narrator's friend, Kali, feel sorry for them as well?

_____

_____

Page 72: Why doesn't the narrator ever return to the Muslim woman's home to sell vegetables?

_____

_____

3. **Responding to the Selection, page 73.** If you lived in the narrator's village, how would you feel about the changes that are happening there? Would you consider the tannery a blessing or a curse? Explain.

_____

_____

_____

_____

_____

_____

_____

_____

_____

_____

_____

Selection Worksheet

"The Street-Sweeping Show," page 80

READER RESPONSE ACTIVITIES

1. **Reader's Journal, page 81.** Think about a politician or other public figure you have seen in the media promoting a community project, organization, or event. Now, imagine what was going on behind the scenes—what the press did not cover. Write about what you envision going on behind the scenes. Do you believe that the public figure's participation was as wholehearted as it seemed? Why, or why not?

_____

_____

_____

_____

_____

_____

_____

_____

_____

_____

_____

_____

_____

2. **Guided Reading.** Answer these questions as you read the selection.

   Page 81: What does Secretary Zhao ask the mayor to approve?

   _____

   _____

   Page 81: Which group was accidentally left out of the Cleanup Week?

   _____

   _____

   Page 82: Why does the mayor say he will attend the event?

   _____

   _____

Page 82: How many dignitaries are sweeping the square?

_____

_____

Page 82: What makes sweeping this area an unusual task?

_____

_____

Page 82: Who gives a broom to the mayor? What type of broom does the mayor receive?

_____

_____

Page 83: What does the marshal tell the mayor?

_____

_____

Page 83: What "instruction" does the mayor have for the townspeople?

_____

_____

Page 83: How does the mayor feel about the street-sweeping show and his performance?

_____

_____

3. **Responding to the Selection, page 84.** Imagine the mayor and his grandson are having a conversation about what it is like to be mayor. Would he encourage his grandson to go into politics? Imagine that the grandson wants to be mayor. What might his grandfather tell him? Write your responses below.

_____

_____

_____

_____

_____

_____

_____

_____

Selection Worksheet

"The Nose," page 92

READER RESPONSE ACTIVITIES

1. **Reader's Journal, page 93.** If you could change one part of your appearance or personality, what would it be? Why would you like to make this change? Would it be better to learn to accept yourself as you are? Why, or why not?

_____

_____

_____

_____

_____

_____

_____

_____

_____

_____

_____

_____

_____

_____

_____

_____

_____

_____

_____

_____

_____

_____

_____

2. **Guided Reading.** Answer these questions as you read the selection.

Page 93: Why had everyone in the town of Ike-no-O heard of Zenchi Naigu's nose?

_____

_____

Page 93: What do the townspeople say about Zenchi and his decision to become a priest?

_____

_____

Page 93: In what way is Zenchi's nose an intolerable nuisance?

_____

_____

Page 94: What is Zenchi's sole concern in his role as priest?

_____

_____

Page 94: What does Zenchi try to do as he looks at himself in the mirror?

_____

_____

Page 94: Why does Zenchi closely scrutinize the visitors at the Buddhist masses?

_____

_____

Page 95: With what has the disciple become acquainted?

_____

_____

Page 96: What is the formula prescribed by the disciple?

_____

_____

Page 96: How does Zenchi feel about the treatment prescribed by the disciple?

_____

_____

Page 96: What is the result of this unusual "treatment"?

_____

_____

Page 97: How does Zenchi feel about his new appearance?

_____

_____

Page 97: What concern plagues Zenchi?

_____

_____

Page 97: What surprises Zenchi about the reactions of those around him?

_____

_____

Page 97: What does the narrator say about human nature? According to the narrator, why are people now laughing at Zenchi?

_____

_____

_____

Page 98: What does Zenchi do to the page? Why?

_____

_____

Page 98: What has happened to Zenchi's nose overnight?

_____

_____

Page 98: How does Zenchi feel when he realizes what has happened to his nose? Why does he feel this way?

_____

_____

_____

3. **Responding to the Selection, page 99.** If you were a disciple at Zenchi's temple, what advice would you have given him before he shrunk his nose? after?

_____
_____
_____
_____
_____
_____
_____
_____
_____
_____
_____
_____
_____
_____
_____
_____
_____
_____
_____
_____
_____
_____
_____
_____
_____
_____
_____
_____
_____
_____
_____
_____

Selection Worksheet

A Doll's House, act 1, page 110

READER RESPONSE ACTIVITIES

1. **Reader's Journal, page 111.** On the lines below, write about a time when you performed an action and overlooked the consequences of that act. For example you may have decided not to tell a friend the truth. What emotions or reasons led you to perform this action? Why were you willing to overlook the consequences of this act? If you could go back in time, would you do anything differently? Why, or why not?

_____

_____

_____

_____

_____

_____

2. **Guided Reading.** Answer these questions as you read the selection.

   Page 111: What do you think the people who live in this house are like?

   _____

   _____

   Page 112: What pet names does Torvald Helmer have for his wife? What do these pet names reveal about Nora? about Torvald?

   _____

   _____

   Page 112: How does Torvald feel about borrowing money?

   _____

   _____

   Page 112: Does Torvald take Nora's emotions seriously?

   _____

   _____

   Page 113: What is Torvald saying about Nora? To what is he comparing her?

   _____

   _____

Page 113: What is Nora eager to have for Christmas?

_____

_____

Page 113: About what is Torvald concerned?

_____

_____

Page 114: Is Nora telling Torvald the truth? What do you think about the way Torvald is questioning Nora?

_____

_____

Page 114: What are Nora and Torvald happy about?

_____

_____

Page 115: Why does Nora ask Christine Linde to forgive her?

_____

_____

Page 115: What is Christine saying about her deceased husband?

_____

_____

Page 116: What does Nora say she is going to do? What does she do instead?

_____

_____

Page 116: What happened to Torvald?

_____

_____

Page 116: What does Christine say about Nora?

_____

_____

Page 117: Why does Christine respond this way to Nora?

_____

_____

Page 117: What does Christine want from Nora?

_____

_____

Page 117: What have the last few years been like for Christine? How does this compare with what Nora has revealed of her life?

_____

_____

Page 118: What has Christine said that upsets Nora?

_____

_____

Page 118: What is Nora happy and proud of doing? How do you think she got the money?

_____

_____

Page 118: What can't a woman do without her husband's consent? What does Nora imply?

_____

_____

Page 119: When did Torvald become "almost angry" with Nora?

_____

_____

Page 119: Why did Nora have to borrow money without Torvald knowing?

_____

_____

Page 120: According to Nora, why can't she tell Torvald about the money she borrowed?

_____

_____

Page 120: How does Nora feel about working to earn money?

_____

_____

Page 120: When does Nora say she will tell Torvald about what she has done?

_____

_____

Page 121: How does Christine seem to feel about Krogstad?

_____

_____

Page 121: How does Nora seem to feel about Krogstad?

_____

_____

Page 122: What amuses Nora?

_____

_____

Page 122: In what way does Dr. Rank describe Krogstad?

_____

_____

Page 122: How would you characterize Nora's mood?

_____

_____

Page 123: In what way do Nora's and Torvald's reactions to the children differ?

_____

_____

Page 124: What is Nora's reaction to Krogstad's arrival?

_____

_____

Page 124: Why does Krogstad's remark seem threatening?

_____

_____

Page 125: In whom is Krogstad interested?

_____

_____

Page 125: What does Krogstad ask of Nora? Whom does he blame for his dismissal? Why?

_____

_____

Page 126: Why is Krogstad's job so important to him?

_____

_____

Page 126: From whom did Nora borrow the money?

_____

_____

Page 126: What was one of the conditions of the loan?

_____

_____

Page 127: What crime has Nora committed?

_____

_____

Page 128: What does Krogstad say about Nora's crime?

_____

_____

Page 128: What attitude does Nora take toward the law and her crime in front of Krogstad?

_____

_____

Page 129: How does Nora feel about her conversation with Krogstad? Why is she concerned that her home appear beautiful and that she appear happy?

_____

_____

Page 129: How does Torvald feel about Krogstad? about Nora's agreeing to intercede on Krogstad's behalf?

_____

_____

Page 130: Why does Nora ask Torvald these questions?

_____

_____

Page 131: What does Nora tell herself about what Torvald has said? What does she tell Anne-Marie to do with the children?

_____

_____

3. **Responding to the Selection, page 131.** Do you think Torvald and Nora have a good relationship by today's standards? Why, or why not? If you could give both Torvald and Nora some advice about their relationship, what would you say?

_____

_____

_____

_____

_____

_____

_____

_____

_____

_____

_____

_____

_____

_____

_____

_____

_____

_____

_____

Selection Worksheet

A Doll's House, act 2, page 133

READER RESPONSE ACTIVITIES

1. **Reader's Journal, page 133.** How do you feel about keeping secrets? Do they make you nervous? excited? Have you ever had something you wanted kept secret revealed? How did the revelation make you feel? Have you ever revealed something that somebody else wished to keep secret? What were the ramifications of your actions?

_____

_____

_____

_____

2. **Guided Reading.** Answer these questions as you read the selection.

Page 133: Why does Nora say she won't be able to spend time with her children? Why does she ask these questions about her children?

_____

_____

Page 134: Why doesn't Nora dare to go out?

_____

_____

Page 134: What is wrong with Dr. Rank?

_____

_____

Page 135: In what way does Nora's relationship with Dr. Rank differ from her relationship with Torvald?

_____

_____

Page 136: What does Mrs. Linde think about Nora's relationship with Dr. Rank?

_____

_____

Page 136: What is Nora thinking about doing?

_____

_____

Page 137: What kind of a person does Torvald claim to be? What does he think of himself?

_____

_____

Page 137: According to Torvald, why does Nora's request make it impossible for him to keep Krogstad?

_____

_____

Page 138: What is Torvald's real reason for wanting to dismiss Krogstad?

_____

_____

Page 138: What does Nora think of Torvald's reasoning? Do you agree with her?

_____

_____

Page 138: What does Torvald say about himself? In what way does Nora interpret this remark?

_____

_____

Page 139: What is wrong with Dr. Rank? Why doesn't he want anyone to see him? What will he do to notify the Helmers of his condition?

_____

_____

Page 140: What does Nora say Dr. Rank should imagine? How does Nora feel about Dr. Rank?

_____

_____

Page 141: How does Dr. Rank feel about Nora?

_____

_____

Page 141: How does Dr. Rank feel about helping and advising Nora?

_____

_____

Page 141: Did Nora know that Dr. Rank felt this way? Why won't she let him help her?

_____

_____

Page 142: What did Dr. Rank think about Nora?

_____

_____

Page 142: To what does Nora compare her love for Torvald?

_____

_____

Page 143: What does Krogstad say he plans to do with his knowledge of Nora's crime?

_____

_____

Page 144: What does Krogstad want to blackmail Torvald into doing?

_____

_____

Page 144: What has Nora been thinking of doing? Why does she say that she has the courage now?

_____

_____

Page 145: What does Nora ask Christine to do?

_____

_____

Page 145: What does Krogstad drop in the letter box?

_____

_____

Page 145: What does Nora say is about to happen? What does Nora say about this thing?

_____

Page 145: What does Christine say about Krogstad?

_____

_____

Page 146: What does Nora do to keep Torvald from opening the letter box?

_____

_____

Page 147: What does Torvald say about Nora's dancing? In what way is he right?

_____

_____

Page 148: What can Torvald tell from Nora's behavior? What does Nora ask of Torvald? Why does Dr. Rank try to convince Torvald?

_____

_____

Page 148: Why do you think Nora is determined to behave wildly and with abandon?

_____

_____

3. **Responding to the Selection, page 148.** Do you sympathize with Nora's situation? Why, or why not? What would you do if you were in her position?

_____

_____

_____

_____

_____

_____

_____

_____

_____

_____

_____

_____

Selection Worksheet

A Doll's House, act 3, page 150

READER RESPONSE ACTIVITIES

1. **Reader's Journal, page 150.** On the lines below, write about a time when you became disillusioned with someone or something. What happened to make you lose your belief in this person or thing? In what way did this experience change you?

   _____

   _____

   _____

   _____

   _____

2. **Guided Reading.** Answer these questions as you read the selection.

   Page 150: What relationship used to exist between Christine and Krogstad? What happened to end this relationship?

   _____

   _____

   Page 151: Why did Christine come to town? What does she need to make life worth living?

   _____

   _____

   Page 151: What is Christine suggesting?

   _____

   _____

   Page 152: What is Krogstad suspicious that Christine is doing?

   _____

   _____

   Page 152: Why does Christine tell Krogstad that he should not ask for the letter back?

   _____

   _____

Page 153: In what way does Christine disappoint Nora's hopes?

_____

_____

Page 154: What advice does Torvald give to Christine? What do you think of his giving this advice?

_____

_____

Page 154: What does Torvald say Nora is doing? What is he implying about her?

_____

_____

Page 154: What does Torvald call Nora?

_____

_____

Page 155: Is Torvald happy to see his "dearest friend"? How do you know?

_____

_____

Page 155: What experiment does Nora know Dr. Rank has been carrying out?

_____

_____

Page 156: Why does Nora tell Dr. Rank to sleep well? Why does she ask him to wish her the same?

_____

_____

Page 156: What does Dr. Rank mean by this statement?

_____

_____

Page 157: Who do you think feels worse about Dr. Rank's approaching death? Who was the better friend to Dr. Rank?

_____

_____

Page 157: What does Torvald say he wishes for?

_____

_____

Page 158: What is Nora beginning to understand?

_____

_____

Page 158: What is Nora contemplating? Why would this be a terrible thing to do to the others around her?

_____

_____

Page 158: For whom is Torvald most concerned? What does Torvald say when Nora promises that he will be free when she is "gone from this world"?

_____

_____

Page 158: In what way does Torvald respond when Nora tells him how much she loved him and how she does not want him to suffer for her sake?

_____

_____

Page 159: What does Torvald think of what Nora has been through?

_____

_____

Page 159: What plans does Torvald make for the future?

_____

_____

Page 159: In what way does Torvald change his plans after reading the second letter?

_____

_____

Page 160: What does Torvald say he will do? Do you think Nora believes him?

_____

_____

Page 160: What does Nora find unusual?

_____

_____

Page 160: What does Torvald say about forgiveness?

_____

_____

Page 161: What does Nora say about their house?

_____

_____

Page 161: What does Nora say has been done to her? According to Nora, how did her father and her husband feel about her?

_____

_____

Page 161: What does Nora say about Torvald?

_____

_____

Page 161: Why didn't Nora ever show her father that she had opinions? What did Nora's father call her? In what way does she describe her marriage to Torvald?

_____

_____

_____

Page 161: What does Nora say she must do?

_____

_____

Page 162: What doesn't Nora believe anymore? What does she believe?

_____

_____

Page 162: What duty is, to Nora, as sacred as the duty she owes to her husband and to her children?

_____

_____

Page 162: In what way do Nora and Torvald differ? Which character do you most respect, and why?

_____

_____

_____

Page 163: What was the "miracle" Nora had hoped for?

_____

_____

Page 163: What makes Nora so certain of her position at this point in the play? What has she learned about the beliefs of her husband and of the society around her?

_____

_____

_____

Page 163: What does Torvald say about this "miracle"? What does Nora point out?

_____

_____

_____

Page 163: Why has Torvald lost Nora's love?

_____

_____

Page 164: What does Nora say about her relationship to Torvald? Why must she leave?

_____

_____

_____

Page 164: What doesn't Nora believe in anymore?

_____

_____

Page 164: What is the "miracle of miracles"?

_____

_____

3. **Responding to the Selection, page 165.** What do you think of Nora's decision to leave? Is it the right decision? If you were in her position, would you stay or would you go? Why?

_____

_____

_____

_____

_____

_____

_____

_____

_____

_____

_____

_____

_____

_____

_____

_____

_____

_____

_____

_____

_____

_____

_____

_____

_____

_____

_____

_____

_____

RESPONDING IN WRITING

1. **Prewriting: Dramatic Scene, page 166.** Use the space below to freewrite about two characters whose personal qualities you wish to reveal.

_____

_____

_____

_____

_____

_____

_____

_____

_____

_____

_____

_____

_____

_____

_____

_____

_____

_____

_____

_____

2. **Prewriting: Critical Essay, page 166.** Do a focused freewrite about Torvald's character and Nora's character in the space below. Answer the following questions: Which character seems to be more ethical at the play's beginning? Which character seems to be more ethical at the play's end? Which character is more concerned with outer respectability? Which character is more concerned with inner respectability? Why does Torvald condemn Nora? Why does Nora become disillusioned with Torvald?

_____

_____

_____

_____

_____

_____

_____

_____

_____

_____

_____

_____

_____

_____

_____

_____

_____

_____

_____

_____

_____

_____

_____

_____

_____

Now, state your thesis and at least three main ideas for your supporting paragraphs on the lines provided.

Thesis:

_____

_____

Main Idea 1:

_____

_____

Main Idea 2:

_____

_____

Main Idea 3:

_____

_____

Selection Worksheet

Requiem, page 168

READER RESPONSE ACTIVITIES

1. **Reader's Journal, page 169.** Have you ever been separated from somebody whom you love? Have you ever feared for the safety of a close friend or family member? Think about a time when you experienced one or both of these situations. On the lines below, write about the situation and the feelings you had.

   _____

   _____

   _____

   _____

   _____

   _____

   _____

   _____

2. **Guided Reading.** Answer these questions as you read the selection.

   Page 169: Where was the speaker during the time to which she refers? How does she feel about this place?

   _____

   _____

   Page 169: What does the woman want the speaker to do?

   _____

   _____

   Page 170: What experiences do the women not share with other people? Why are these experiences not part of the lives of the waiting women?

   _____

   _____

   Page 170: Who was glad during this time? Why were these people happy?

   _____

   _____

Page 171: Whom does the speaker say she will be like? In what way will she be like them?

_____

_____

Page 172: Why is the woman alone?

_____

_____

Page 172: What is the speaker's reaction in this stanza?

_____

_____

Page 172: What was the speaker's childhood like? In what way do the events of her adult life contrast with her childhood?

_____

_____

_____

Page 172: What has the speaker done since her son was arrested? What does the speaker fear will happen?

_____

_____

_____

Page 173: What does the speaker say that she is unable to comprehend?

_____

_____

Page 173: How does the speaker react to the sentence? What must the speaker do?

_____

_____

Page 173: Why does the speaker invite death?

_____

_____

Page 174: In what ways might death come?

_____

_____

Page 175: What effect has the strain and sorrow had on the speaker?

_____

_____

Page 176: To what mother does the speaker refer?

_____

_____

Page 176: What does the speaker recognize about her experience?

_____

_____

Page 176: What purpose does this poem serve, according to the speaker?

_____

_____

Page 177: Where does the poet want to be remembered? Why do you think she chooses this place?

_____

_____

Page 177: What mood is expressed in the last few lines of the poem?

_____

_____

3. **Responding to the Selection, page 178.** Which poem from this poetic cycle did you find most powerful or moving? What emotions did this section of *Requiem* evoke in you? Which images were particularly powerful, and why?

_____

_____

_____

_____

_____

_____

_____

_____

_____

_____

RESPONDING IN WRITING

1. **Prewriting: Requiem, page 179.** Use the space below to complete a focused freewrite about someone or something that has been lost to you. Consider the following questions: What words describe the lost person, place, or thing? What qualities made the person, place, or thing special? What effect did the person, place, or thing have on you? What effect did he, she, or it have on others or on the world? How do you feel without the person, place, or thing?

_____

_____

_____

_____

_____

_____

_____

_____

_____

_____

_____

_____

2. **Prewriting: Critical Essay, page 179.** Organize your research about Anna Akhmatova into a time line of her life in the space below. For more information on time lines, see the Language Arts Survey 1.10, "Gathering Ideas." Highlight or circle any events that you think are related to *Requiem*.

EVENTS IN THE LIFE OF ANNA AKHMATOVA

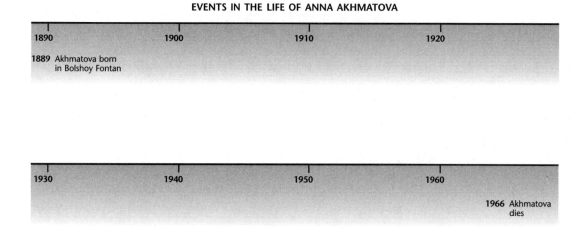

Selection Worksheet

2.5

from *Night*, page 181

READER RESPONSE ACTIVITIES

1. **Reader's Journal, page 182.** Elie Wiesel has said that "if we forget [the Holocaust], we are guilty, we are accomplices." What do you think he means by this statement? Why is it so important for people to remember the Holocaust? On the lines below, write your thoughts about the Holocaust and why it should be remembered.

   _____

   _____

   _____

   _____

   _____

   _____

   _____

   _____

   _____

   _____

   _____

2. **Guided Reading.** Answer these questions as you read the selection.

   Page 182: What expectations do the people on the train have about their future?

   _____

   _____

   Page 183: What additional information does Madame Schächter give about her vision?

   _____

   _____

   Page 183: What does Madame Schächter say she sees? Do the other people see what she sees?

   _____

   _____

   Page 183: How do the other people on the train react to Madame Schächter's cries?

   _____

   _____

Page 184: Where does the train stop? What do the people on the train learn about this place?

_____

_____

Page 185: What does Madame Schächter scream as the train stops? What do the other people on the train finally see?

_____

_____

Page 186: What does the narrator believe cannot happen to people? Why does his father disagree?

_____

_____

Page 186: What do the narrator and his father now know about Madame Schächter?

_____

_____

Page 186: What effect does the first night in camp have on the narrator?

_____

_____

3. **Responding to the Selection, page 187.** What words or images made the greatest impression on you? In the space below, jot down these images and describe the effect this selection had on you.

_____

_____

_____

_____

_____

_____

_____

_____

_____

_____

_____

_____

RESPONDING IN WRITING

1. **Prewriting: Editorial or Speech, page 188.** In order to get your ideas flowing about the injustice you feel strongly about, work with a partner to role play a discussion about this injustice. Your partner should pretend to be unaware of this injustice and should elicit your thoughts and feelings about this issue, noting them down on the lines below. Use your partner's notes about your conversation as the starting point for your speech.

_____

_____

_____

_____

_____

_____

_____

_____

_____

_____

_____

_____

_____

_____

_____

_____

_____

_____

_____

_____

_____

_____

_____

2. Prewriting: Critical Essay, page 188. In the space below, create a formal outline for your essay on the narrator's and his family's disbelief about their fates. If you need more information on formal outlines, review the Language Arts Survey, 1.12, "Outlining." Continue the outline that has been begun for you below as necessary.

I. _____

   A. _____

      1. _____

      2. _____

   B. _____

      1. _____

      2. _____

II. _____

_____

_____

_____

_____

_____

_____

_____

_____

_____

_____

_____

_____

_____

_____

_____

_____

_____

_____

_____

_____

_____

Selection Worksheet

2.6

from *The Bluest Eye*, page 189

READER RESPONSE ACTIVITIES

1. **Reader's Journal, page 190.** If you could change one of your characteristics, either a physical characteristic or a personality trait, which one would you change? Why? In what way do you think that this change would affect your life?

_____

_____

_____

_____

_____

_____

_____

_____

_____

_____

2. **Guided Reading.** Answer these questions as you read the selection.

Page 190: What does Pecola wish would happen?

_____

_____

Page 190: How does Pecola feel about herself? What effect does she think her physical characteristics have on her life?

_____

_____

Page 191: What has Pecola prayed for every night for a year?

_____

_____

Page 191: According to the narrator, what effect does Pecola's wish have on her life?

_____

_____

Page 191: In what way does Pecola think her life would be different if she had pretty eyes?

_____

_____

Page 192: What is Mr. Yacobowski unable to do?

_____

_____

Page 193: What emotions is Pecola feeling? What does she think about the dandelions now?

_____

_____

Page 193: What does Pecola realize about Mr. Yacobowski's gaze?

_____

_____

Page 193: What is anger better than? Why?

_____

_____

Page 193: Why does Pecola love to eat Mary Janes?

_____

_____

3. **Responding to the Selection, page 194.** Imagine that you are Pecola's friend. What advice would you give her about her life? What would you say if you had an opportunity to speak to her teachers? to Mr. Yacobowski?

_____

_____

_____

_____

_____

_____

_____

_____

_____

_____

Name _____ Class _____ Date _____

_____

_____

_____

_____

_____

_____

_____

_____

_____

_____

_____

_____

_____

_____

_____

_____

_____

_____

RESPONDING IN WRITING

1. **Prewriting: Children's Story, page 195.** Fill in details about your culturally diverse children's story in the story map below.

Story Map

Setting and Mood

Time _____

_____

Place _____

_____

Mood _____

_____

Conflict ____ internal ____ external

_____

Major characters

_____

_____

Plot
Inciting incident _____

Climax _____

Resolution _____

_____

Themes _____

_____

2. **Prewriting: Critical Essay, page 195.** Compare and contrast the effects of apartheid as portrayed in *Kaffir Boy* with the effects of racism as presented in *The Bluest Eye* in the Venn diagram below.

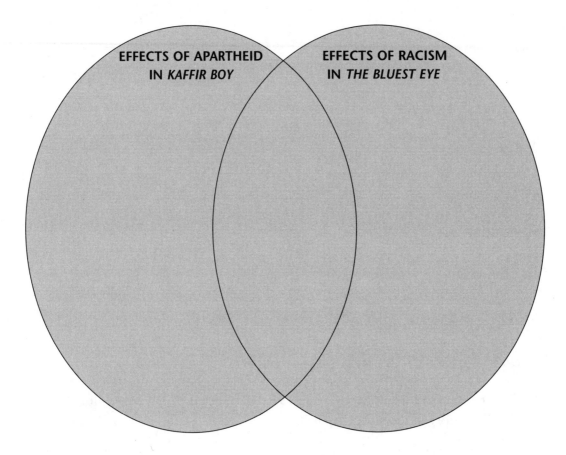

EFFECTS OF APARTHEID IN *KAFFIR BOY*

EFFECTS OF RACISM IN *THE BLUEST EYE*

Selection Worksheet

from *Kaffir Boy*, page 196

READER RESPONSE ACTIVITIES

1. **Reader's Journal, page 197.** Imagine that you live in a place and time in which you are discriminated against based on whether or not you have dimples. For example, if you don't have dimples, you are deprived of certain freedoms and economic and political opportunities. (If you do have dimples, imagine that it is your group instead that is experiencing this oppression.) Then respond to the following questions: How would you feel about yourself and your dimples or lack thereof? How would you feel about your oppressors? What would you think of the laws that limited opportunities or created opportunities, depending on your dimples?

_____

_____

_____

_____

_____

_____

_____

_____

_____

_____

_____

_____

2. **Guided Reading.** Answer these questions as you read the selection.

   Page 197: Of what did the narrator have a childhood dread?

   _____

   _____

   Page 197: Why did the narrator begin to assume that white people were not so bad? What word does he use to qualify the Smiths' kindness?

   _____

   _____

Page 197: What does the narrator's grandmother mean by "trouble"?

_____

_____

Page 198: What does Granny say to the bus driver? In what tone of voice must she say it? What does the bus driver say that he could do?

_____

_____

Page 198: What mistake has the narrator made? In what way does the bus driver react to the narrator's mistake?

_____

_____

Page 198: What makes the situation seem particularly unreal to the narrator?

_____

_____

Page 198: What does the narrator's grandmother say about him? What does she do that horrifies the narrator?

_____

_____

Page 199: What does the narrator wonder?

_____

_____

Page 200: What reason does Granny give the narrator for her outburst? What does she say *apartheid* means?

_____

_____

Page 200: What does Granny say about the phone booths?

_____

_____

Page 200: Why does the narrator wonder how his grandmother functions normally? To what is the narrator's consciousness awakened?

_____

_____

3. **Responding to the Selection, page 201.** Imagine that you are a friend of the narrator in this selection. What advice would you give him after his grandmother tells him how apartheid works? Would you advise him to follow the rules of apartheid? Would you advise him to organize nonviolent protests against apartheid, or would you tell him to do something else?

_____

_____

_____

_____

_____

_____

_____

_____

_____

_____

_____

RESPONDING IN WRITING

1. **Prewriting: Letter of Complaint, page 202.** Use the following chart to jot down your ideas before drafting your letter of complaint.

Complaints about Bus Company

_____

_____

SUGGESTIONS FOR BUS COMPANY	REASONS WHY BUS COMPANY SHOULD MAKE THESE CHANGES
_____	_____
_____	_____
_____	_____
_____	_____
_____	_____
_____	_____
_____	_____
_____	_____
_____	_____

2. Prewriting: Critical Essay, page 202. Organize your ideas for an essay about Granny's attitude toward apartheid in the space below.

Thesis: _____

Main Idea 1: _____

_____

Evidence or Quotation Supporting This Idea

_____

_____

_____

_____

_____

Main Idea 2: _____

_____

Evidence or Quotation Supporting This Idea

_____

_____

_____

_____

_____

Main Idea 3: _____

_____

Evidence or Quotation Supporting This Idea

_____

_____

_____

_____

_____

_____

Selection Worksheet

2.8

"By Any Other Name," page 204

READER RESPONSE ACTIVITIES

1. **Reader's Journal, page 205.** How do you identify yourself? To what groups or classifications do you belong? Have you ever been treated unfairly because of one of these classifications? Classifications might include gender, age, race, ability, financial status, or physical characteristics. Write about an experience you have had with discrimination.

   _____

   _____

   _____

   _____

   _____

   _____

   _____

   _____

   _____

   _____

   _____

   _____

   _____

2. **Guided Reading.** Answer these questions as you read the selection.

   Page 205: Why does the headmistress say she makes the change that she does?

   _____

   _____

   Page 206: In what way are the Indian children different from the British children?

   _____

   _____

   Page 206: Why had the narrator's mother refused to send her children to a British school until this point? What happened to change her mind?

   _____

   _____

Page 206: What effect did the name change have on the narrator?

_____

_____

Page 207: Why doesn't the narrator understand the meaning of winning? What difficulty does this cause her?

_____

_____

Page 209: What causes Premila to leave the school?

_____

_____

Page 210: What was the narrator's attitude toward this incident? Why did she feel this way?

_____

_____

3. **Responding to the Selection, page 210.** What do you think about Premila's decision to leave the school? Do you think that doing so was a good way to handle the problem? How would you have reacted had you been in her place? Respond to these questions in the space provided.

_____

_____

_____

_____

_____

_____

_____

_____

_____

_____

_____

_____

_____

_____

_____

RESPONDING IN WRITING

1. **Prewriting: Personal Essay, page 211.** Use the space below to freewrite about events from your childhood that made an impression on you.

_____

_____

_____

_____

_____

_____

_____

_____

_____

_____

_____

_____

_____

_____

_____

_____

_____

_____

_____

_____

_____

_____

_____

_____

_____

_____

_____

_____

_____

Name _____ Class _____ Date _____

2. Prewriting: Critical Essay, page 211. Fill in the cluster chart below with your ideas about the significance of names. Add more circles or spokes as necessary.

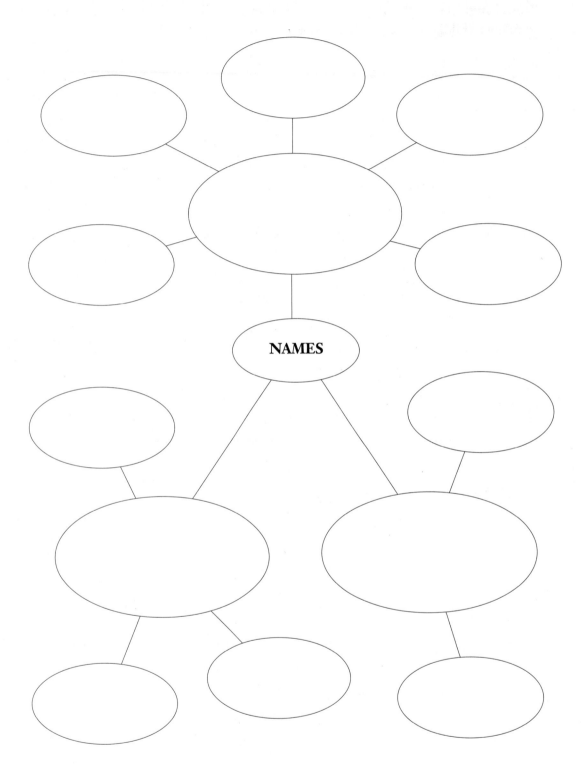

NAMES

Selection Worksheet

3.1

from the *Aeneid*, page 222

READER RESPONSE ACTIVITIES

1. **Reader's Journal, page 223.** What happens to a relationship when the people involved find that they have completely different goals and values? Do you think people should follow their hearts and stay involved at all costs or stay true to their individual goals? Is it possible to do both? Explain your response. You may use examples from your own life or from books and movies.

_____

_____

_____

_____

_____

_____

_____

_____

_____

2. **Guided Reading.** Answer these questions as you read the selection.

   Page 224: What does Mercury find Aeneas doing?

   _____

   _____

   Page 224: To what does Mercury accuse Aeneas of being oblivious?

   _____

   _____

   Page 225: What must Aeneas tell Queen Dido?

   _____

   _____

   Page 225: What are Aeneas's men to keep secret? Why does Aeneas want them to keep this secret?

   _____

   _____

Page 225: What does Dido find out on her own? What is her reaction to the information?

_____

_____

Page 226: What does Dido do to try to get Aeneas to stay with her?

_____

_____

Page 227: Why does Dido believe that Aeneas should take pity on her? What has happened as a result of their relationship?

_____

_____

Page 227: Is Aeneas happy to be going? Is he leaving of his own free will?

_____

_____

Page 228: Where exactly is Aeneas going? Why does he believe that Dido should understand what motivates him to leave?

_____

_____

Page 228: Why is Aeneas's trip "not of [his] own free will"?

_____

_____

Page 229: What does Dido say to Aeneas about his trip? Does she wish him well? Explain.

_____

_____

Page 229: How does Aeneas feel about leaving Dido when she is so upset?

_____

_____

Page 230: What question does the narrator ask about love? In what way is Dido going to humble her pride?

_____

_____

Page 231: What does Dido ask her sister Anna to say to Aeneas? What happens when Anna goes to Aeneas?

_____

_____

Page 232: Is Aeneas moved by Dido's request? Does he change his plans?

_____

_____

Page 232: For what does Dido pray after she is sure Aeneas will leave? What act does she plan to perform?

_____

_____

Page 232: What voices does Dido hear? About what does she have nightmares?

_____

_____

Page 233: To what type of ritual does Dido turn in her desperation?

_____

_____

Page 234: What does Dido ask her sister to build? What does she tell her sister she plans to do?

_____

_____

Page 234: Why does Anna build the pyre? What is Anna's mistake?

_____

_____

Page 235: To whom does Dido call out? For what does she want justice?

_____

_____

Page 236: Why can't Dido sleep?

_____

_____

Page 236: Why does Dido feel her situation is hopeless?

_____

_____

Page 236: Why can Aeneas sleep while Dido cannot?

_____

_____

Page 237: What does Mercury tell Aeneas?

_____

_____

Page 237: What does Aeneas do in response to Mercury's advice and comment?

_____

_____

Page 238: What does Dido feel that Aeneas has done by leaving?

_____

_____

Page 238: What does Dido wish she had done?

_____

_____

Page 239: What vow does Dido make about Aeneas and his people?

_____

_____

Page 240: What is "the enormous thing afoot"?

_____

_____

Page 240: What does Dido say about her life? What does she wish never happened? What does Dido plan to do, and what effect does she want this action to have on Aeneas?

_____

_____

Page 241: Why does Dido's sister Anna feel deceived? For what does she wish?

_____

_____

Page 242: Why does Juno take pity on Dido? Whom does she send to Dido, and for what purpose?

_____

_____

3. **Responding to the Selection, page 243.** How do you feel about the relationship between Aeneas and Queen Dido? Do you sympathize more with Dido or with Aeneas? Explain your response.

_____

_____

_____

_____

_____

_____

_____

_____

_____

_____

_____

_____

_____

_____

_____

_____

_____

_____

_____

_____

_____

_____

RESPONDING IN WRITING

1. **Prewriting: Journal Entries, page 244.** Before you write your journal entry from your chosen character's point of view, fill in the character chart below.

   My chosen character: _____

   My character's personal traits: _____

   _____

   _____

   _____

What is happening in my character's life?

_____

_____

_____

_____

How might my character react to these situations?

_____

_____

_____

_____

_____

_____

_____

_____

_____

_____

2. **Prewriting: Critical Essay, page 244.** Use the lines below to do a focused freewrite on the following questions: What critical moment in the excerpt starts Dido's downward spiral into madness and toward her ultimate destruction? Why was it impossible for her to change Aeneas's mind about their relationship? In what way is her inability to accept his change of plans destructive to herself and to others? How does Virgil show her emotional state becoming worse and worse?

_____

_____

_____

_____

_____

_____

_____

_____

_____

_____

_____

_____

_____

_____

Selection Worksheet

"The River-Merchant's Wife: A Letter," page 245

READER RESPONSE ACTIVITIES

1. **Reader's Journal, page 246.** Have you ever been separated from a close friend or family member for a long time? What thoughts and concerns go through your mind when you are separated from a person who is important to you? Write on the lines below about how it feels to miss someone.

_____

_____

_____

_____

_____

_____

_____

_____

_____

2. **Guided Reading.** Answer these questions as you read the selection.

   Page 246: What did these two people do when they were younger? How long ago did they meet?

   _____

   _____

   Page 246: Why do you think the speaker "looked at the wall" and "never looked back" when called to?

   _____

   _____

   Page 246: When and in what way did the speaker's feelings about her marriage change?

   _____

   _____

   Page 246: For how long has the speaker's husband been gone?

   _____

   _____

Page 247: Why is the moss at the gate now overgrown? Of what does this moss become a symbol?

_____

_____

Page 247: What will the speaker do if she hears that her husband is coming along the river Kiang?

_____

_____

3. **Responding to the Selection, page 248.** How did you feel while reading this poem? Imagine that the speaker is a friend who has just shared her feelings with you. Write a response to the speaker, offering advice or just lending support.

_____

_____

_____

_____

_____

_____

_____

_____

_____

_____

_____

_____

_____

_____

_____

_____

_____

_____

_____

RESPONDING IN WRITING

1. **Prewriting: Letter Poem, page 249.** Use the space below to freewrite about your chosen character, his or her story, and the person to whom he or she wishes to write a letter.

_____

_____

_____

_____

_____

_____

_____

_____

_____

_____

_____

_____

_____

_____

_____

_____

_____

_____

_____

_____

_____

_____

_____

_____

_____

_____

2. **Prewriting: Critical Essay, page 249.** To determine what the poet reveals about the river-merchant's wife as a character, ask and answer the so-called reporting questions about the wife, her situation, and her feelings.

Who? _____

_____

Answer: _____

_____

What? _____

Answer: _____

_____

Where? _____

Answer: _____

_____

When? _____

Answer: _____

_____

Why? _____

Answer: _____

_____

How? _____

Answer: _____

_____

Selection Worksheet

3.3

from the *Canzoniere*, page 251

READER RESPONSE ACTIVITIES

1. **Reader's Journal, page 252.** Describe a person for whom you have felt great love or admiration. What is special about this person? Did you ever have to face the thought of not having this person in your life? If yes, explain your experience. If no, try to imagine what life would be like without this person.

_____

_____

_____

_____

_____

_____

_____

_____

_____

_____

2. **Guided Reading.** Answer these questions as you read the selection.

   Page 252: Whom does the speaker address in this poem? To what does the speaker fall captive on this day?

   _____

   _____

   Page 252: Where does the speaker find his cue?

   _____

   _____

   Page 252: Was the speaker prepared for love? Is he comfortable with these feelings? What is the response of the lady with whom he has fallen in love?

   _____

   _____

   Page 253: Whom or what is the speaker addressing in this poem?

   _____

   _____

Page 253: Why is the speaker envious? What or who was taken from him?

_____

Page 253: What do earth, heaven, souls in heaven, and death have to do with the speaker's loss? What does he envy?

_____

_____

3. **Responding to the Selection, page 254.** Suppose the speaker had written his feelings in a journal, rather than in the form of two sonnets. What might he have entered in his journal about the feelings expressed in the poems? Write a journal entry expressing Petrarch's feelings.

_____

_____

_____

_____

_____

_____

_____

_____

_____

_____

_____

_____

_____

_____

_____

_____

_____

_____

_____

_____

RESPONDING IN WRITING

1. **Prewriting: Lyric Poem, page 255.** Fill in the chart below with possible subjects for a lyric poem and your feelings about these people.

POSSIBLE SUBJECTS	MY REACTIONS, THOUGHTS, AND FEELINGS

2. **Prewriting: Critical Essay, page 255.** To classify the images that Petrarch uses to express pain, loss, and frustration, list these images in the appropriate columns in the sensory detail chart below.

SENSORY DETAIL CHART: IMAGES USED BY PETRARCH				
SIGHT	SOUND	TOUCH	TASTE	SMELL

Selection Worksheet

"Though I am Laila of the Persian romance," page 257

READER RESPONSE ACTIVITIES

1. **Reader's Journal, page 258.** When you think of the word *love*, what are some images—words that name things that can be seen, heard, touched, tasted, or smelled—that come to mind? List images commonly associated with romantic love. Identify some unique images of your own that express or describe romantic love.

_____

_____

_____

_____

_____

_____

_____

2. **Guided Reading.** Answer these questions as you read the selection.

   Page 258: Who is the speaker? What is her heart like?

   _____

   _____

   Page 258: Where does the speaker want to go? What chains her feet?

   _____

   _____

   Page 258: In what is the speaker an expert?

   _____

   _____

3. **Responding to the Selection, page 259.** What is the speaker of the poem like? What adjectives might you use to describe her feelings about herself and about love? Explain your choices.

   _____

   _____

   _____

   _____

RESPONDING IN WRITING

1. **Prewriting: "Though I am . . ." Poem, page 260.** Use the space below to brainstorm a list of your personality traits. Try to list at least five or six.

_____

_____

_____

_____

_____

_____

_____

_____

_____

_____

_____

2. **Prewriting: Critical Essay, page 260.** In the Venn diagram below, compare and contrast the experiences and feelings about love of Zeb-un-Nissa and the speaker of "The River-Merchant's Wife: A Letter."

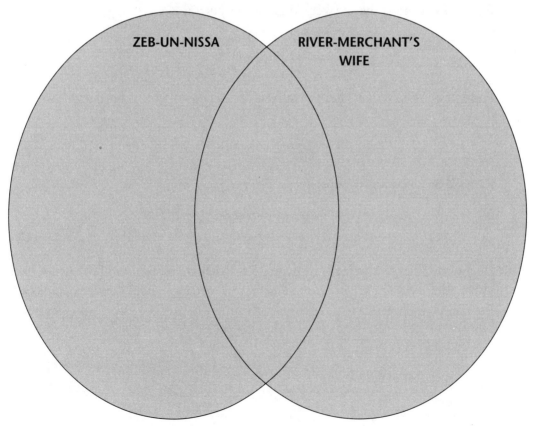

ZEB-UN-NISSA

RIVER-MERCHANT'S WIFE

Selection Worksheet

"Tonight I Can Write," page 261

READER RESPONSE ACTIVITIES

1. **Reader's Journal, page 262.** Think about the last time you felt sad and lonely. Then freewrite images—words that name things that can be seen, heard, touched, tasted, or smelled—that remind you of these feelings. For example, you might list things like an abandoned building; a dark, empty street; or the call of a bird.

_____

_____

_____

_____

_____

_____

_____

_____

_____

_____

_____

2. **Guided Reading.** Answer these questions as you read the selection.

   Page 262: What type of verse might the speaker write tonight? What example of such verses does he give?

   _____

   _____

   Page 262: Did the woman the speaker describes ever love him? What is one feature that he loved about her?

   _____

   _____

   Page 262: According to the speaker, what is the night like without his beloved? To what does he compare his verse?

   _____

   _____

Page 263: What does the speaker hear in the distance? How does he feel about having lost this woman?

_____

_____

Page 263: What does the speaker say about the woman's current situation?

_____

_____

Page 263: What is important about the pain the speaker feels and the verses that he writes tonight?

_____

_____

3. **Responding to the Selection, page 264.** How does this poem make you feel? Cite a line from the poem that you find especially vivid and heartfelt and tell why you find it so.

_____

_____

_____

_____

_____

_____

_____

_____

_____

_____

_____

_____

_____

_____

_____

_____

_____

RESPONDING IN WRITING

1. **Prewriting: Mood Paragraph or Poem, page 265.** Fill in the chart below with specific moods and images that capture your chosen moods. Then, use your ideas listed in the chart as inspiration for your mood poem or paragraph.

MOOD	IMAGES
_____	1. _____ 2. _____ 3. _____
_____	1. _____ 2. _____ 3. _____
_____	1. _____ 2. _____ 3. _____
_____	1. _____ 2. _____ 3. _____
_____	1. _____ 2. _____ 3. _____
_____	1. _____ 2. _____ 3. _____

2. **Prewriting: Critical Essay, page 265.** To organize your response to the essay, fill in the chart below.

Central conflict of the poem: _____

_____

_____

_____

Words and phrases that portray this conflict: _____

_____

_____

_____

_____

_____

_____

_____

_____

_____

_____

_____

_____

_____

_____

_____

_____

_____

_____

_____

_____

_____

_____

_____

Selection Worksheet

3.6

"Penelope's Despair," page 266

READER RESPONSE ACTIVITIES

1. **Reader's Journal, page 267.** When was the last time you felt disappointed or let down? Did an exciting or happy event end too soon? Did a person, place, or occasion fail to meet your expectations? On the lines below, describe the experience and your emotional responses to the experience.

_____

_____

_____

_____

_____

_____

_____

_____

_____

_____

_____

_____

_____

_____

_____

_____

2. **Guided Reading.** Answer these questions as you read the selection.

   Page 267: What type of disguise is Odysseus, the subject of the poem, wearing? Why is Penelope able to recognize him despite this?

   _____

   _____

   Page 267: What question does Penelope ask herself?

   _____

   _____

Page 267: Who lies dead on the floor? What of Penelope lies dead on the floor as well?

_____

_____

Page 267: What does Penelope say to Odysseus? How does her voice sound?

_____

_____

3. **Responding to the Selection, page 268.** Suppose you were one of Penelope's close friends. What might she say to you about the night of Odysseus's return? How might she now feel about the time she spent waiting for him?

_____

_____

_____

_____

_____

_____

_____

_____

_____

_____

_____

_____

_____

_____

_____

_____

_____

_____

_____

_____

RESPONDING IN WRITING

1. **Prewriting: Point of View Experiment, page 269.** Fill in the chart below with interview questions you would like to ask your chosen character about what happens in the work you have chosen, his or her feelings about the situation, and his or her point of view. Use the so-called reporting questions: who? what? where? when? why? and how? Then, try to imagine your chosen character's responses.

Work: _____

Point of view from which the work is originally told: _____

Character whose point of view I wish to explore: _____

Q: _____

A: _____

_____

Q: _____

A: _____

_____

Q: _____

A: _____

_____

Q: _____

A: _____

_____

Q: _____

A: _____

_____

Q: _____

A: _____

_____

2. **Prewriting: Critical Essay, page 269.** On the lines below, freewrite about Penelope's character, focusing upon her motivations for waiting for Odysseus and her feelings about his return. Respond to the following questions: Does Penelope's twenty-year wait for Odysseus make her strong and virtuous or foolish and pitiful? Why might she be experiencing unexpected feelings on Odysseus's return?

_____

_____

_____

_____

_____

_____

_____

_____

_____

_____

_____

_____

_____

_____

_____

_____

_____

_____

_____

_____

_____

_____

_____

_____

_____

_____

_____

_____

Selection Worksheet

3.7

"The Little Heidelberg," page 270

READER RESPONSE ACTIVITIES

1. **Reader's Journal, page 271.** Describe an interesting or unusual place that you have seen or visited. When did you see or visit this place? What is most special about it, the actual place or the people whom you saw or met there? On the lines below, write a letter to a friend in which you describe this place in detail.

_____

_____

_____

_____

_____

_____

_____

_____

_____

_____

_____

_____

_____

2. **Guided Reading.** Answer these questions as you read the selection.

   Page 271: Why was it difficult to believe that El Capitán and *niña* Eloísa had never spoken a single word?

   _____

   _____

   Page 271: What clothing do the musicians wear?

   _____

   _____

   Page 271: Where is The Little Heidelberg located? What food is served there?

   _____

   _____

Page 272: What is the median age of the women at the tavern? What does their age not diminish?

_____

_____

Page 272: What do the teenagers do when they visit the tavern? Why do they leave?

_____

_____

Page 272: What do the musicians play? Why does this music seem out of place?

_____

_____

Page 272: Who are the people that make up the tavern's clientele?

_____

_____

Page 273: Who is the oldest client of The Little Heidelberg? What has she spent her life doing?

_____

_____

Page 273: When did *niña* Eloísa come to the village?

_____

_____

Page 273: How important is language and conversation at The Little Heidelberg?

_____

_____

Page 273: What are the rules of the dance floor? What is understood about the woman called La Mexicana?

_____

_____

Page 273: How do people at The Little Heidelberg feel about *niña* Eloísa?

_____

_____

Page 274: Who is particularly drawn to the Scandinavian tourist couple that visits the tavern one December Saturday?

_____

_____

Page 275: What is the reaction of the regulars at the tavern to the couple's news?

_____

_____

Page 275: What does El Capitán ask *niña* Eloísa? What is her first response? What does she finally say?

_____

_____

Page 275: What happens to *niña* Eloísa as she dances with El Capitán?

_____

_____

Page 276: Why do the musicians continue to play the special waltz? What does La Mexicana do?

_____

_____

3. **Responding to the Selection, page 276.** What do you think of The Little Heidelberg tavern and its clientele? What was your impression of El Capitán and his relationship with *niña* Eloísa?

_____

_____

_____

_____

_____

_____

_____

_____

_____

_____

RESPONDING IN WRITING

1. **Prewriting: Description, page 277.** Use the sensory detail chart below to capture vivid images of the place you have imagined.

SENSORY DETAIL CHART				
SIGHT	SOUND	TOUCH	TASTE	SMELL

2. **Prewriting: Critical Essay, page 277.** Use the chart below to jot down details from the story that are purely realistic or purely fantastic, as well as details that combine elements of realism and fantasy.

REALISTIC DETAILS	FANTASTIC DETAILS	DETAILS INTERMINGLING REALITY AND FANTASY

Selection Worksheet

"Love after Love," page 279

READER RESPONSE ACTIVITIES

1. **Reader's Journal, page 280.** What do you like most about yourself? On the lines below, record as many positive aspects of yourself as you can. Why is it important to remind oneself of these things from time to time?

_____

_____

_____

_____

_____

_____

_____

_____

_____

_____

_____

_____

_____

_____

2. **Guided Reading.** Answer these questions as you read the selection.

Page 280: According to the speaker, what time will come? Who will be greeted at the door?

_____

_____

Page 280: What does the speaker say must be given back to "itself"? According to the speaker, whom should the subject of the poem learn to love again?

_____

_____

Page 280: What items should be discarded? What should be peeled from the mirror?

_____

_____

3. Responding to the Selection, page 281. "Sit. Feast on your life." What does this line from Walcott's poem mean to you? Explain why this poem might be encouraging to someone who is experiencing rejection or a difficult relationship with another person.

_____

_____

_____

_____

_____

_____

_____

_____

_____

_____

_____

_____

_____

_____

_____

_____

_____

_____

_____

_____

_____

_____

_____

_____

_____

_____

_____

_____

_____

RESPONDING IN WRITING

1. **Prewriting: "Feast on Your Life" Poem, page 283.** On the lines below, freewrite about the person who is having a difficult time. What troubles this person? What special qualities does he or she possess? How might you make this person feel better about himself or herself?

_____

_____

_____

_____

_____

_____

_____

_____

_____

_____

_____

_____

_____

_____

_____

_____

_____

_____

_____

_____

_____

_____

_____

_____

_____

_____

_____

2. **Prewriting: Critical Essay, page 283.** Organize your ideas for this essay using a formal outline. If you need more information on formal outlines, review the Language Arts Survey, 1.12, "Outlining." Continue the outline that has been begun for you below as necessary.

    I. _____

      A. _____

         1. _____

         2. _____

      B. _____

         1. _____

         2. _____

    II. _____

_____

_____

_____

_____

_____

_____

_____

_____

_____

_____

_____

_____

_____

_____

_____

_____

_____

_____

_____

Selection Worksheet

"The Weighing of the Heart of Ani," page 296

READER RESPONSE ACTIVITIES

1. **Reader's Journal, page 297.** On the lines below, write about a time when your character was judged by others. Why were you judged? What did others have to say about your character? Did you think the judgment was fair? Why, or why not? Explain how you felt about the results of this judgment.

_____

_____

_____

_____

_____

_____

_____

_____

_____

_____

_____

_____

_____

_____

_____

2. **Guided Reading.** Answer these questions as you read the selection.

   Page 297: What is being evaluated at this judgment?

   _____

   _____

   Page 297: What does the speaker mean by "May the Sheniu officials . . . not cause my name to stink"?

   _____

   _____

© 1998 EMC Corporation

Page 298: What is the finding of this judgment?

_____

_____

Page 298: What punishment do those who do evil receive?

_____

_____

3. **Responding to the Selection, page 300.** What do you think of the Egyptian passage to the afterlife as it is portrayed in this selection? If you were in Ani's position, what would you say to convince the gods to spare you from Ām-mit?

_____

_____

_____

_____

_____

_____

_____

_____

_____

_____

_____

_____

_____

_____

_____

_____

_____

_____

_____

_____

_____

_____

_____

_____

RESPONDING IN WRITING

1. **Prewriting: Character Sketch, page 301.** Before you begin drafting, complete the following cluster chart. Fill in the name of your character in the center circle. Then add details about your character's personality, emotions, life, and appearance.

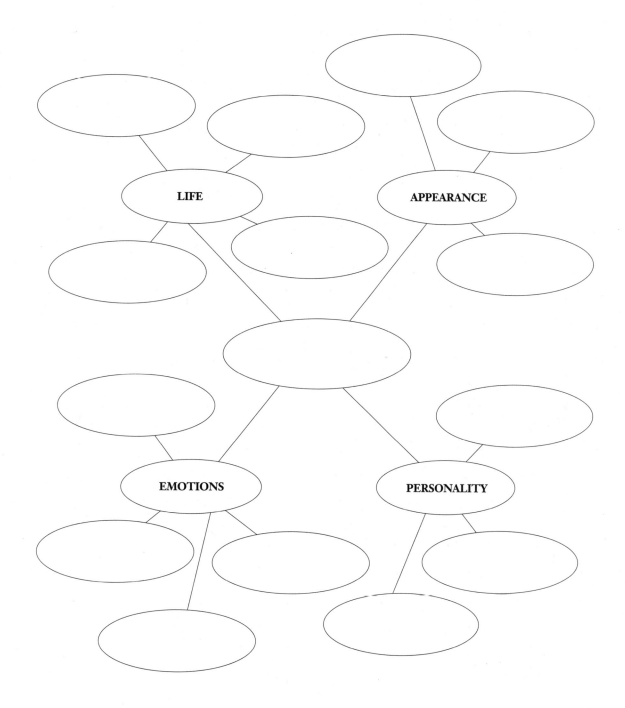

Name _____ Class _____ Date _____

2. Prewriting: Critical Essay, page 301. After choosing a topic from those suggested in your book, complete the following outline of your essay. Use your own paper and add headings and subheadings as necessary.

Thesis: _____

_____

I. _____

   A. _____

      1. _____

      2. _____

   B. _____

      1. _____

      2. _____

II. _____

_____

_____

_____

_____

_____

_____

_____

_____

_____

_____

_____

_____

_____

_____

_____

_____

_____

_____

Selection Worksheet

"The Death of Socrates," page 303

READER RESPONSE ACTIVITIES

1. **Reader's Journal, page 304.** Imagine that you knew that you would die within a few hours. What instructions or advice would you give to your family or friends as the time of your death approached? In what way might they best honor your memory?

_____

_____

_____

_____

_____

_____

_____

_____

_____

_____

_____

_____

2. **Guided Reading.** Answer these questions as you read the selection.

   Page 304: What can Socrates's followers do to please him?

   _____

   _____

   Page 304: What assurance does Socrates ask his followers to give Crito?

   _____

   _____

   Page 304: What does Socrates say about being buried after his death?

   _____

   _____

   Page 305: How do Socrates's followers feel about losing him?

   _____

   _____

Page 305: What does the prison officer say about Socrates? Of what is the prison officer sure?

_____

_____

Page 306: What does Socrates think of his captor, the prison officer?

_____

_____

Page 306: Why does the narrator weep?

_____

_____

Page 306: Why doesn't Socrates want to wait until evening to drink the poison?

_____

_____

Page 306: What is Socrates's reaction to his friends' tears?

_____

_____

Page 307: In what way does the narrator sum up Socrates's character?

_____

_____

3. **Responding to the Selection, page 308.** What do you think of the way in which Socrates approaches and meets his death? If you were in his position, would you hope to emulate his attitudes and actions, or would you want to behave differently? Explain.

_____

_____

_____

_____

_____

_____

_____

_____

_____

_____

_____

_____

_____

_____

_____

_____

_____

_____

_____

_____

_____

_____

RESPONDING IN WRITING

1. **Prewriting: Dialogue, page 309.** After choosing the person to whom you would like to speak, freewrite about the following questions: What has his or her experience after death been like? What kind of life did this person lead on earth? Did the person's life on earth affect his or her experiences after death? What is one thing this person might want to change about his or her life? How did the person die? What was it like passing from life into death?

_____

_____

_____

_____

_____

_____

_____

_____

_____

_____

_____

_____

_____

_____

_____

_____

_____

_____

_____

_____

_____

_____

_____

_____

_____

2. **Prewriting: Critical Essay, page 309.** Before you begin writing, complete the chart below with examples from the selection that seem like fiction and elements that seem like nonfiction.

ELEMENTS OF FICTION	ELEMENTS OF NONFICTION

Selection Worksheet

"Lament for His Son," page 310

READER RESPONSE ACTIVITIES

1. **Reader's Journal, page 311.** Why is it especially sad when a person dies young, before he or she has lived a full life? What experiences and opportunities might someone who dies young miss? On the lines below, explain your feelings about untimely death.

   _____

   _____

   _____

   _____

   _____

   _____

2. **Guided Reading.** Answer these questions as you read the selection.

   Page 311: What does the speaker say it was his turn to do? What happened instead? What does the speaker say he has become without his son?

   _____

   _____

   Page 311: What does the speaker believe his son has done in the afterlife? Why does the speaker believe his son is angry with him?

   _____

   _____

3. **Responding to the Selection, page 312.** Explain whether the speaker in this selection evokes your sympathy. Do you think he deals with his grief well? Explain why or why not.

   _____

   _____

   _____

   _____

   _____

   _____

RESPONDING IN WRITING

1. **Prewriting: Sympathy Card, page 313.** In the space below, freewrite about your sympathy for the speaker.

_____

_____

_____

_____

_____

_____

_____

_____

_____

_____

_____

_____

2. **Prewriting: Critical Essay, page 313.** After choosing which path you will encourage the speaker to take, brainstorm a list of reasons to convince him to take this path. In the chart below circle the heading appropriate for the path you have chosen and list your reasons and examples in the space provided.

REASONS TO FOLLOW SON TO AFTERLIFE	REASONS TO ENJOY LIFE

Selection Worksheet

from *The Death of Iván Ilyich*, page 314

READER RESPONSE ACTIVITIES

1. **Reader's Journal, page 315.** What is a meaningful life? What is a superficial life? What is a strong, genuine relationship? What is an artificial, shallow relationship? Can the pursuit of superficial goals and relationships be destructive to an individual and to society? Explain your answer.

_____

_____

_____

_____

_____

_____

_____

2. **Guided Reading.** Answer these questions as you read the selection.

Page 315: When do Iván Ilyich's bursts of temper occur? To what does his wife, Praskóvya Fëdorovna, attribute these bursts of temper?

_____

_____

Page 315: What accompanies the pressure in Iván Ilyich's side? How does the mood in his home change as a result of this discomfort?

_____

_____

Page 316: For what does Iván's wife wish? Why does she consider herself dreadfully unhappy?

_____

_____

Page 316: What does Iván conclude from the doctor's explanation of his problem? How does this conclusion make him feel? What does he ask the doctor?

_____

_____

Page 316: Of what does the doctor's behavior remind Iván?

_____

_____

Page 317: What becomes the focus of Iván's life? What does he do when he hears people talk about illness?

_____

_____

Page 317: How do the things he sees in the streets seem to Iván as he drives home? Why has his ache acquired new significance?

_____

_____

Page 317: What are the attitudes of his wife and daughter as Iván describes his meeting with the doctor?

_____

_____

Page 317: What three things continually interfere with Iván's efforts to force himself to feel better?

_____

_____

Page 318: What seems to make Iván's condition worse? Why?

_____

_____

Page 318: What torments Iván more than anything else?

_____

_____

Page 318: What incident causes Iván to fear that his mind has weakened?

_____

_____

Page 318: What does Iván's wife say about his behavior and his ability to care for himself?

_____

_____

Page 319: What is Praskóvya Fëdorovna's attitude toward Iván's illness?

_____

_____

Page 319: What does Iván notice about his treatment by friends and colleagues?

_____

_____

Page 320: What ought to have made Iván feel jolly and lively? Why doesn't it?

_____

_____

Page 320: What does Iván realize about his life?

_____

_____

Page 320: Where is Iván forced to live? What is he forced to live without?

_____

_____

3. **Responding to the Selection, page 320.** "And he had to live thus all alone on the brink of an abyss, with no one who understood or pitied him." Do you think this statement reflects Iván Ilyich's situation? Why, or why not? How do you feel toward Iván Ilyich? How do you feel about the people in his life?

_____

_____

_____

_____

_____

_____

_____

RESPONDING IN WRITING

1. **Prewriting: Memorial, page 322.** Freewrite about your subject's qualities, accomplishments, and relationships. Then review your freewriting and chose three or four things that you think are most important to include in your memorial.

_____

_____

_____

_____

_____

_____

_____

_____

Most important things about subject:

1. _____

2. _____

3. _____

4. _____

2. **Prewriting: Critical Essay, page 322.** To help you gather and organize your ideas for this essay, answer the following questions.

1. What does Iván do for a living?

_____

2. What kinds of things had Iván valued most in his life before his illness?

_____

_____

3. What kind of relationship does he have with his wife and family?

_____

_____

_____

4. Does he have many close friends?

_____

5. How do people feel about Iván's illness?

_____

_____

6. Why do people have these feelings?

_____

_____

_____

Selection Worksheet

from *The Sound of the Mountain*, page 323

READER RESPONSE ACTIVITIES

1. **Reader's Journal, page 324.** Do you enjoy lingering over your memories, or do you focus more on the present and the future? How would you feel if your memory grew dim and you were unable to recall clear images from the past? On the lines below, explain whether a loss of memory would affect your life profoundly, or whether this loss would have little effect in your life.

_____

_____

_____

_____

_____

_____

_____

_____

_____

_____

_____

2. **Guided Reading.** Answer these questions as you read the selection.

   Page 324: How would Ogata Shingo appear to a stranger? What does Shuichi realize Shingo is doing? Why does Shuichi give "little thought" to what is happening?

   _____

   _____

   Page 324: What is Shingo trying to remember? What does he say he is unable to do? What does Shuichi think of his father's claim?

   _____

   _____

   Page 325: Why doesn't Shuichi feel sympathy for his father? How does Shingo feel when he cannot remember the girl?

   _____

   _____

Page 325: How does Shingo feel about this symptom—spitting blood? Why won't he see a doctor? What does Shuichi think of his father's behavior?

_____

_____

Page 325: What habit did Shingo's wife, Yasuko, have when she was younger? When does she resume this habit?

_____

_____

Page 326: What saddens Shingo?

_____

_____

Page 326: What is happening too early in the season?

_____

_____

Page 327: How does Shingo feel when he hears this sound?

_____

_____

Page 327: What does the mountain sound like?

_____

_____

3. **Responding to the Selection, page 327.** Do you feel sympathy for Shingo? If you were in Shuichi's position, would you feel and behave as he does, or would you feel and act differently toward your father?

_____

_____

_____

_____

_____

_____

_____

_____

Name _____ Class _____ Date _____

_____

_____

_____

_____

_____

_____

RESPONDING IN WRITING

1. **Prewriting: Symbols, page 328.** Work with others to brainstorm a list of conventional symbols for death. To come up with personal symbols, begin by filling in the cluster chart with things you associate with death.

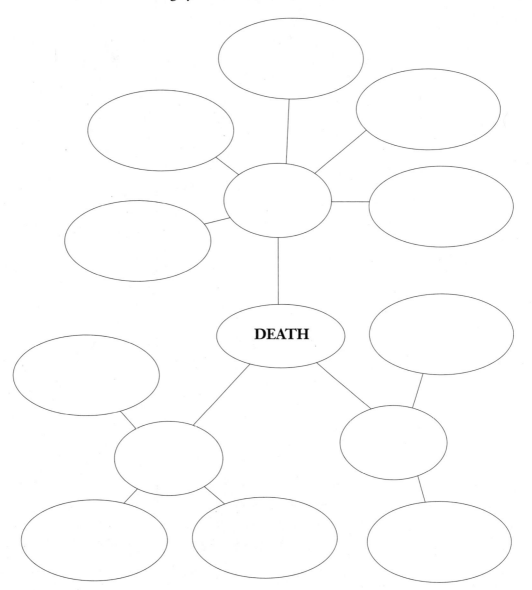

2. **Prewriting: Critical Essay, page 329.** To begin this essay, first identify the common characteristics of the tanka and haiku poetry. Consider such aspects of the works as mood, tone, and imagery. Then identify ways in which the selection from *The Sound of the Mountain* is similar to these works. Fill in the chart below.

SIMILAR ASPECT OF WORK	EXAMPLE FROM TANKA/HAIKU	EXAMPLE FROM KAWABATA

Selection Worksheet

"Life Is Sweet at Kumansenu," page 330

READER RESPONSE ACTIVITIES

1. **Reader's Journal, page 331.** Describe a situation in which you followed your own instincts instead of the advice or opinions of others. Why did you do this? Did everything work out for the best? Why, or why not?

_____

_____

_____

_____

_____

_____

_____

_____

_____

2. **Guided Reading.** Answer these questions as you read the selection.

Page 331: Where is this story set? What kinds of houses are in the village?

_____

_____

Page 331: How many of Bola's infant sons died?

_____

_____

Page 331: What does Bola believe about the deaths? On the birth and death of her sixth child, what did the village magician advise Bola to do? Did Bola follow his advice?

_____

_____

Page 332: What does Bola notice on the body of her seventh child? What becomes of this child? What is his name?

_____

_____

Page 332: Why does Meji leave his daughter Asi with Bola?

_____

_____

Page 332: What does Meji say to Bola when he hears that she wants to tell the neighbors about his visit?

_____

_____

Page 332: What reason does Meji give for this secrecy?

_____

_____

Page 333: What worry does Bola have about Meji's visit? What is Meji's response?

_____

_____

Page 333: What does Bola notice about Meji?

_____

_____

Page 334: Where does Meji take Asi while Bola goes to market?

_____

_____

Page 334: Why does Bola want to bring Meji to his father's grave? What does she want her husband to know about their son?

_____

_____

Page 334: What does Asi notice about Meji's shadow? What does she notice about his watch and his neck?

_____

_____

Page 334: What does Meji say about his father?

_____

_____

Page 334: What does Bola notice outside her son's window? What does she say?

_____

_____

Page 335: What does Mr. Addai come to tell Bola? Why doesn't Bola believe him?

_____

_____

Page 335: What does Meji tell his mother as he stands on the veranda, "curiously unwet"?

_____

_____

Page 335: What is the crowd's opinion about Bola's claim that she had just seen her son? How did Meji die? What does Asi shout out about her father?

_____

_____

Page 336: What does Asi's mother give her? What does Asi try to remember? What does Mrs. Meji angrily tell the child?

_____

_____

Page 336: What does Musa the magician tell Bola she should have done thirty-one years ago?

_____

_____

Page 336: According to Bola, why did her son come back? About what is she glad? Why doesn't she expect Musa to understand?

_____

_____

3. **Responding to the Selection, page 336.** If you were in Bola's position, would you wish that you had never had a seventh son to die young and leave you in grief, or would you be happy to have been able to enjoy him during his brief life? Explain your reasoning.

_____

_____

_____

_____

_____

_____

_____

_____

_____

RESPONDING IN WRITING

1. **Prewriting: Sharing a Ritual, Tradition, or Belief, page 338.** On the lines below, freewrite about rituals, traditions, and beliefs of your family or community. If you have already chosen a subject, do a focused freewrite on that topic.

_____

_____

_____

_____

_____

_____

_____

_____

_____

_____

_____

_____

_____

2. **Prewriting: Critical Essay, page 338.** Fill in the chart below as you reread the story.

FORESHADOWING	EFFECT

Selection Worksheet

"Tuesday Siesta," page 339

READER RESPONSE ACTIVITIES

1. **Reader's Journal, page 340.** Describe a situation in which you felt like an outsider. Why did you feel this way? Why did you feel unwelcome or uncomfortable in your surroundings? What effect did these feelings have on your behavior? On the lines below, explain how you felt in that situation.

_____

_____

_____

_____

_____

_____

_____

_____

_____

_____

_____

_____

2. **Guided Reading.** Answer these questions as you read the selection.

   Page 340: What do the mother and her daughter wear?

   _____

   _____

   Page 340: What could be seen on the narrow road? At what time of day is the train traveling?

   _____

   _____

   Page 341: Why does the girl go to the washroom? What does she do just before she goes to the washroom?

   _____

   _____

Page 341: What does the woman tell her daughter she must not do once they reach their destination?

_____

_____

Page 342: In what does the girl wrap her flowers? What happens when she stares at her mother?

_____

_____

Page 342: At what time of day do the mother and daughter step off the train? What is going on in the town?

_____

_____

Page 342: Why does the priest want the mother and daughter to come back later? Why are they unable to do that?

_____

_____

Page 342: Where do the girl and her mother immediately go?

_____

_____

Page 343: What do they need from the priest? Why does he feel that they should wait?

_____

_____

Page 343: What had Carlos's last words been? What had he been wearing?

_____

_____

Page 343: Whose grave do they want to visit? How is the deceased known to the priest?

_____

_____

Page 343: Who killed Carlos? Why?

_____

_____

Page 343: What kind of man does Carlos's mother feel he was?

_____

_____

Page 344: What was one of the rules Carlos was taught by his mother? What did he do on Saturday nights before he became a thief?

_____

_____

Page 344: Why do the priest and his sister want the woman and her daughter to wait before they leave?

_____

_____

Page 344: Who is gathered outside the priest's house?

_____

_____

3. **Responding to the Selection, page 345.** Explain whether the mother in this story is an admirable character. Why do you feel as you do about this character?

_____

_____

_____

_____

_____

_____

_____

_____

_____

_____

_____

_____

_____

_____

_____

_____

RESPONDING IN WRITING

1. **Prewriting: Description, page 346.** In the space below, sketch the layout of your village or town. Include any important buildings, natural features, or other landmarks. Then, on your own paper, freewrite on each of the following topics: What are the inhabitants of the village or town like? What is the mood or atmosphere of the village or town? What is the history of the village or town?

2. **Prewriting: Critical Essay, page 346.** First identify the mood of the story. Then review the story, and as you do so jot down examples of imagery that contribute to this mood.

MOOD: _____	
IMAGERY	EFFECT

Selection Worksheet

"Rice Pudding," page 347

READER RESPONSE ACTIVITIES

1. **Reader's Journal, page 348.** Choose one member of your family. Think about your interaction with this person yesterday. Write as much as you can remember about what this person looked like, what he or she was doing, and what he or she said. Try to remember details of the person's appearance, voice, and exact words. How did you feel while you were with this person?

_____

_____

_____

_____

_____

_____

_____

_____

_____

_____

_____

_____

_____

_____

_____

_____

_____

2. **Guided Reading.** Answer these questions as you read the selection.

   Page 348: What does the narrator choose to call the man? Why is this name appropriate?

   _____

   _____

   Page 348: What words does the man remember? Why does he repeat these words?

   _____

   _____

Page 349: What emotion suddenly overcomes the man? Why does he curse his wife?

_____

_____

Page 349: What happens when the man thinks of his sons? How does the man feel about his reaction?

_____

_____

Page 349: How does the man view his wife's death? How does he feel about his responsibilities?

_____

_____

Page 349: What questions do the man's sons ask when he returns home? Why is he surprised by these questions?

_____

_____

Page 350: Why does the father offer to make new food for his sons? Do the children understand what has happened to their mother?

_____

_____

3. **Responding to the Selection, page 351.** Imagine that you are a friend of this family. What would you do to help the father deal with his sons? What might you do to comfort them and help them to understand?

_____

_____

_____

_____

_____

_____

_____

_____

_____

_____

_____

_____

_____

_____

_____

_____

_____

_____

_____

_____

_____

RESPONDING IN WRITING

1. **Prewriting: Eulogy, page 352.** To write a meaningful eulogy, try to understand the character well. Before you begin writing, complete the following chart with details about the character.

CHARACTER: _____
Character's values
Character's actions
Character's effect on others

2. **Prewriting: Critical Essay, page 352.** Review "Rice Pudding" and the other work about which you will write. Then fill in the Venn diagram below. Use your own paper if you need additional room.

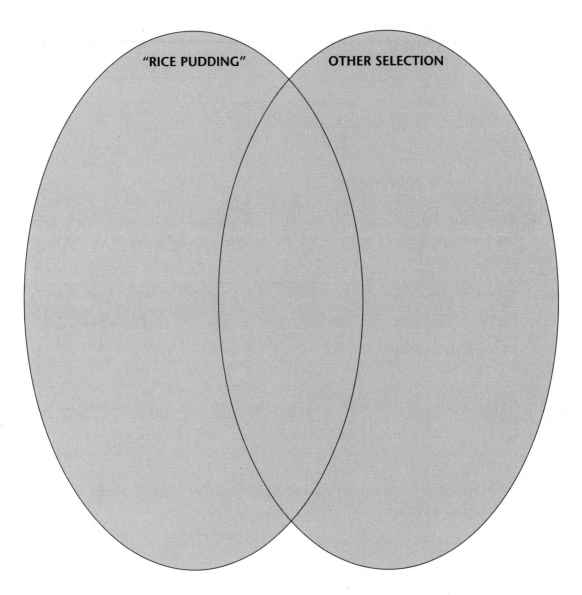

"RICE PUDDING"   OTHER SELECTION

Selection Worksheet

from "Hymn to the Sun," page 364

READER RESPONSE ACTIVITIES

1. **Reader's Journal, page 365.** Imagine that you know no scientific explanation for the rising and the setting of the sun. What might you think the sun is? How might you explain its rising and setting? Where might you think the sun goes when it sets?

_____

_____

_____

_____

_____

_____

2. **Guided Reading.** Answer these questions as you read the selection.

   Page 365: According to the speaker, when did life begin?

   _____

   _____

   Page 365: How far does the sun reach? What do you think Akhenaten means by this statement?

   _____

   _____

   Page 366: What happens after the sun goes down, according to the speaker?

   _____

   _____

   Page 366: According to the speaker, how many gods are there?

   _____

   _____

   Page 367: What does Akhenaten ask of Aten?

   _____

   _____

Page 367: To what does the speaker compare the sun-disk?

_____

_____

3. **Responding to the Selection, page 368.** If you could go back in time to speak with Akhenaten, what questions would you ask him about his religion, Aten worship? What information might you share with him about the sun? What do you think Akhenaten's reaction might be?

_____

_____

_____

_____

_____

_____

_____

_____

_____

_____

_____

_____

_____

_____

_____

_____

_____

_____

_____

_____

_____

_____

_____

RESPONDING IN WRITING

1. **Prewriting: Hymn, page 369.** Before composing your hymn, gather ideas and concrete details about the aspect of nature that you have chosen. Begin by completing the sensory detail chart below. Then, on the following lines, freewrite about why this aspect of nature is important to you.

ASPECT OF NATURE				
SIGHT	SOUND	TOUCH	TASTE	SMELL

_____

_____

_____

_____

_____

_____

_____

_____

_____

_____

_____

_____

_____

_____

_____

_____

_____

_____

2. **Prewriting: Critical Essay, page 369.** To decide which side of the question you will take, complete the following chart with examples that support each option. If you have already made this decision, fill in the chart based on your thesis.

	LIFE-GIVING FORCE	PERSONIFIED GOD
Stanza I		
Stanza II		
Stanza III		
Stanza XI		
Stanza XII		

Selection Worksheet

"I Built My Cottage among the Habitations of Men," page 372

READER RESPONSE ACTIVITIES

1. **Reader's Journal, page 373.** What do you do when you need to escape from the world and relax? What is the place or activity that refreshes you and helps you to think more clearly? Describe this special place or activity. Why might it be important for people to have such places and activities?

   _____

   _____

   _____

   _____

   _____

2. **Guided Reading.** Answer these questions as you read the selection.

   Page 373: Why is it puzzling that the speaker does not hear the "clamor of carriages and horses"? Why doesn't the speaker hear these noises?

   _____

   _____

   Page 373: In what things does the speaker find "deep meaning"? Why are these things important to the speaker?

   _____

   _____

3. **Responding to the Selection, page 374.** Which do you prefer, quiet solitude or activity and company, or do you welcome each at different times? Are you similar to or different from the speaker of this poem?

   _____

   _____

   _____

   _____

   _____

   _____

   _____

Name _____ Class _____ Date _____

RESPONDING IN WRITING

1. **Prewriting: Pastoral Piece, page 375.** Begin by gathering sensory details about your favorite place. Complete the sensory detail chart below. Use these details as you begin to write your pastoral piece.

FAVORITE PLACE				
SIGHT	SOUND	TOUCH	TASTE	SMELL

2. **Prewriting: Critical Essay, page 375.** To write this essay, you need to identify images from the poem and relate them to the theme. First identify the theme and write it at the top of the following chart. Then, as you review the poem, fill in the imagery column of the chart. After you have identified images, make a note in the second column that explains how the image is related to the theme.

THEME: _____	
IMAGE	RELATIONSHIP TO THEME

Selection Worksheet

5.3

Haiku and Tanka, page 378

READER RESPONSE ACTIVITIES

1. **Reader's Journal, page 380.** On the lines below, describe some favorite scenes from nature. For example, you might write about the sky just before a heavy rain shower, a ladybug climbing a blade of grass, a moth on a lampshade, or a flower beginning to wilt. You may either write down images from memory, or spend some time outside observing the natural world before you write.

_____

_____

_____

_____

_____

_____

_____

_____

_____

_____

_____

_____

_____

2. **Guided Reading.** Answer these questions as you read the selection.

Page 380: What noise is created by the frog?

_____

_____

Page 380: What does the speaker hear during the icy night?

_____

_____

Page 380: What does the speaker notice about the first snow?

_____

_____

Page 381: Why is the village flooded with children? What season of year might this poem describe?

_____

_____

Page 381: What disappears in the summer rain? What might cause it to disappear?

_____

_____

Page 381: What causes the cherry tree's petals to "dance" across the sky? To what does the speaker compare the petals?

_____

_____

3. **Responding to the Selection, page 382.** What images from the poems you have just read do you find unique and interesting? Why do you enjoy them?

_____

_____

_____

_____

_____

_____

_____

_____

_____

_____

_____

_____

_____

_____

_____

_____

_____

_____

_____

RESPONDING IN WRITING

1. **Prewriting: Haiku and Tanka, page 383.** You may begin with an image that you have chosen from your Reader's Journal response, or try the following activity. Choose a mood and write it in the center of the cluster chart below. Then in the connected circles jot down images that you associate with this mood. On the rules that follow, experiment with different lines that you might include in your haiku or tanka.

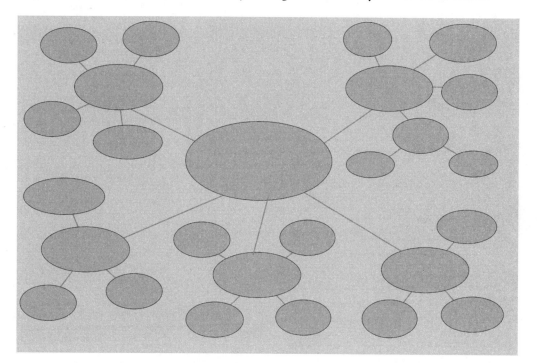

_____

_____

_____

_____

_____

_____

_____

_____

_____

_____

_____

_____

_____

2. **Prewriting: Critical Essay, page 383.** In the chart below, identify the imagery from several haiku poems. Next to each image, jot down your emotional response.

TITLE OF POEM	IMAGE	EMOTIONAL RESPONSE

Selection Worksheet

5.4

"Song Composed in August," page 384

READER RESPONSE ACTIVITIES

1. **Reader's Journal, page 385.** Think about the different kinds of love songs that you have heard. What aspects of nature are often associated with love and romance in these songs and poems? What aspects of nature remind you of love and romance?

   _____

   _____

   _____

   _____

   _____

   _____

   _____

   _____

2. **Guided Reading.** Answer these questions as you read the selection.

   Page 385: At what time of day is the speaker traveling? Whom is the speaker going to see?

   _____

   _____

   Page 385: According to the narrator, who is able to find pleasure?

   _____

   _____

   Page 387: What does the speaker want to do? What things does the speaker say cannot possibly be as dear as his "lovely charmer" is to him?

   _____

   _____

3. **Responding to the Selection, page 388.** Respond to the following questions on the lines below. Is this a poem best read silently or aloud? Explain. What words and phrases from the poem are more vivid read aloud than when read silently?

   _____

   _____

_____

_____

_____

RESPONDING IN WRITING

1. **Prewriting: Love Song, page 389.** Gather concrete details about your subject by freewriting in the space provided.

   Subject: _____

   _____

   _____

   _____

   _____

   _____

   _____

   _____

   _____

   _____

   _____

2. **Prewriting: Critical Essay, page 389.** First answer the question below on the lines provided. Then complete the chart with images from the poem.

   How does the speaker feel about his subject?

   _____

   _____

   _____

IMAGES THAT REFLECT LOVE

Selection Worksheet

"The Iguana," page 390

READER RESPONSE ACTIVITIES

1. **Reader's Journal, page 391.** Have you ever admired something so much that you just had to possess it? What was it that you admired? How did you feel once you had this thing? Did possessing it change your perception of this thing in any way? Respond to these questions on the lines below.

_____

_____

_____

_____

_____

_____

_____

_____

_____

_____

_____

_____

_____

_____

_____

_____

2. **Guided Reading.** Answer these questions as you read the selection.

Page 391: What is noticeable or unique about the iguana? To what does Dinesen compare this characteristic?

_____

_____

Page 391: What did Dinesen buy at Meru? What change seemed to occur to this item once she possessed it?

_____

_____

Page 391: Why did Dinesen hunt the iguana? What happened after she shot it?

_____

_____

Page 392: What advice does Dinesen offer others?

_____

_____

3. **Responding to the Selection, page 393.** In this selection, Dinesen remembers a quote she had read as a child, "I have conquered them all, but I am standing amongst graves." What does this quote mean to you? Describe a time when you felt this way about a situation.

_____

_____

_____

_____

_____

_____

_____

_____

_____

_____

_____

_____

_____

_____

_____

_____

_____

_____

_____

_____

RESPONDING IN WRITING

1. **Prewriting: Anecdote, page 394.** Decide on the message that you would like to share. Then do a focused freewrite about this message to come up with ideas for your anecdote.

   Message: _____

   _____

   _____

   Ideas about message: _____

   _____

   _____

   _____

   _____

   _____

   _____

   _____

   _____

   _____

   _____

   _____

   _____

   _____

   _____

   _____

   _____

   _____

   _____

   _____

   _____

   _____

2. **Prewriting: Critical Essay, page 394.** In the space below, summarize each of the three anecdotes and identify its theme. You may wish to refer to your response to the Understanding Literature question on anecdotes.

Anecdote 1
Summary

_____

_____

_____

_____

Theme

_____

_____

Anecdote 2
Summary

_____

_____

_____

_____

Theme

_____

_____

Anecdote 3
Summary

_____

_____

_____

_____

Theme

_____

_____

Selection Worksheet

"The Flower of Air," page 395

READER RESPONSE ACTIVITIES

1. **Reader's Journal, page 396.** Describe a time when you struggled to accomplish, change, or perfect something. How did it feel to face the struggle? Did you get the results you wanted, or were you disappointed? Explain your responses.

   _____

   _____

   _____

   _____

   _____

   _____

   _____

   _____

   _____

   _____

   _____

   _____

   _____

   _____

   _____

   _____

   _____

   _____

   _____

   _____

   _____

2. **Guided Reading.** Answer these questions as you read the selection.

Page 396: Where does the woman stand? What does she do there?

_____

_____

Page 396: What does the speaker do with the white flowers? What does the woman ask the speaker to bring her next?

_____

_____

Page 397: What happens when the speaker offers the woman the red flowers?

_____

_____

Page 397: To what things does the speaker compare the yellow of the flowers? Is the woman finally satisfied with the yellow flowers?

_____

_____

Page 397: With what does the woman associate the flowers of no color?

_____

_____

Page 398: Where does the speaker get the flowers without color?

_____

_____

Page 399: What is the woman doing when the speaker comes down the mountain?

_____

_____

Page 399: What does the speaker do when the woman walks away?

_____

_____

Page 399: Until when will the speaker follow the woman?

_____

_____

3. Responding to the Selection, page 399. Would you encourage the speaker to continue to struggle to please and follow the woman? Why, or why not? What do you think is the speaker's reward for continuing the struggle?

_____

_____

_____

_____

_____

_____

_____

_____

_____

_____

_____

_____

RESPONDING IN WRITING

1. Prewriting: Images of Nature and Mood, page 401. After you have chosen a scene and a mood, freewrite to gather images.

Place or scene: _____

Mood: _____

Images: _____

_____

_____

_____

_____

_____

_____

_____

_____

Name _____ Class _____ Date _____

2. **Prewriting: Critical Essay, page 401.** This exercise asks you to explain the allegory
   and the way in which the original title and the current title are related to the allegory.
   Think about the attitude implied by each title. Then review the poem and complete
   the chart below by filling in elements from the poem and their symbolic meanings.
   Then relate the information you have gathered to each title.

ELEMENT	MEANING

Selection Worksheet

To "Free-Spirited Fisherman," page 402

READER RESPONSE ACTIVITIES

1. **Reader's Journal, page 403.** What in your life makes you most proud? What in your life makes you least proud? On the lines below, respond to these questions and explain why your feelings are positive or negative toward each thing.

   _____

   _____

   _____

   _____

2. **Guided Reading.** Answer these questions as you read the selection.

   Page 403: What word does the speaker use to describe his or her soul? What question does Heaven ask of the speaker?

   _____

   _____

   Page 403: What is the speaker's opinion about his or her poetry?

   _____

   Page 403: Where does the speaker hope the tiny boat will go?

   _____

3. **Responding to the Selection, page 404.** How do you feel about the ability to write great poems or songs? How does the speaker feel about having this ability? Explain whether you share the speaker's feelings.

   _____

   _____

   _____

   _____

   _____

   _____

RESPONDING IN WRITING

1. **Prewriting: Song Lyrics, page 405.** After choosing a topic, do two focused freewrites about your topic and about why the topic is important to you.

_____

_____

_____

_____

_____

_____

_____

_____

_____

_____

_____

_____

2. **Prewriting: Critical Essay, page 405.** In the chart below list clichéd and original images from the songs that you chose.

CLICHÉD	ORIGINAL

Selection Worksheet

"The Garden of Stubborn Cats," page 406

READER RESPONSE ACTIVITIES

1. **Reader's Journal, page 407.** List some different ways in which civilization interferes with nature. When have you noticed this happening? What steps can people take to protect the natural world? What are the possible consequences if the natural world is not protected?

   _____

   _____

   _____

   _____

   _____

   _____

   _____

   _____

2. **Guided Reading.** Answer these questions as you read the selection.

   Page 407: What two cities are being discussed?

   _____

   _____

   Page 407: What do few cats recall? Of what have domestic cats been prisoners for several generations?

   _____

   _____

   Page 407: What does the city look like? What still scurries through a "network of dry canals on a planet of stucco and tar"?

   _____

   _____

   Page 408: How does Marcovaldo explain the sudden disappearance of the cats? What is he not yet permitted to do?

   _____

   _____

© 1998 EMC Corporation

Page 408: With whom had Marcovaldo made friends? What would he do on his lunch break?

_____

_____

Page 408: In what way had Marcovaldo begun looking at places?

_____

_____

Page 408: What does the tabby lead Marcovaldo to discover? What does he see? Why is everything upside-down?

_____

_____

Page 409: What catches Marcovaldo's attention in the main room?

_____

_____

Page 410: To where does Marcovaldo follow the cat? What does Marcovaldo realize that almost makes him forget his fish?

_____

_____

Page 410: What does the cat watch Marcovaldo do? What does the cat steal?

_____

_____

Page 411: Why, according to the women, are the cats and other animals in the garden?

_____

_____

Page 411: What distracts the cats away from the fish? What happens just when Marcovaldo tries to recover his fish?

_____

_____

Page 411: Who owns the villa? Who wants to buy the villa?

_____

_____

Page 412: What differing opinions are held about the Marchesa?

_____

_____

Page 413: What are the different opinions about the Marchesa's property?

_____

_____

Page 413: What is the Marchesa doing with Marcovaldo's trout? Does she admit to taking the trout?

_____

_____

Page 414: What do the cats do to keep the Marchesa from leaving? Why, according to her, do they want to keep her from leaving?

_____

_____

Page 414: What happens to the garden as soon as the Marchesa dies? What do the cats and other animals do to protest?

_____

_____

3. **Responding to the Selection, page 414.** If you were the official spokesperson for the stubborn cats, what would you say to explain the cats' feelings about the city and their garden? Would you have been happy to keep the garden if you were the Marchesa?

_____

_____

_____

_____

_____

_____

_____

_____

_____

_____

_____

RESPONDING IN WRITING

1. **Prewriting: Description, page 416.** First think of a name for your special place or a phrase that describes the place. Write that name or phrase in the center circle of the cluster chart below. Then jot down ideas related to the ideas in the connected circles. Use some of these details in your description.

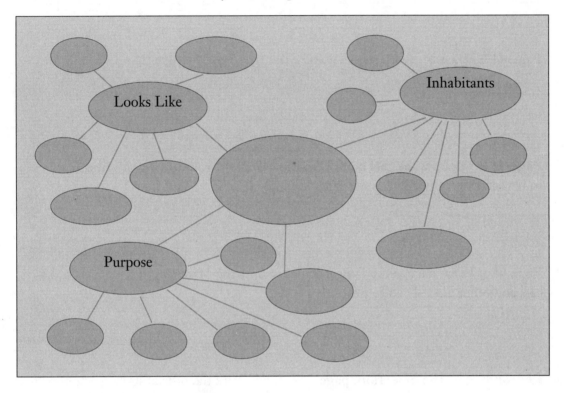

2. **Prewriting: Critical Essay, page 416.** Review the story and make notes in the form of an informal outline about the theme and imagery of the story. For more information on outlining see the Language Arts Survey 1.12, "Outlining."

_____
_____
_____
_____
_____
_____
_____
_____
_____
_____
_____

Selection Worksheet

5.9

"Season," page 417

READER RESPONSE ACTIVITIES

1. **Reader's Journal, page 418.** Describe your favorite season. Why do you enjoy this time of the year? What are some images—sights, sounds, and smells—that come to mind when you think about this particular period of time?

   _____

   _____

   _____

   _____

   _____

2. **Guided Reading.** Answer these questions as you read the selection.

   Page 418: What does the speaker associate with ripeness? What does the speaker associate with pollen?

   _____

   _____

   Page 418: What does the speaker love to hear?

   _____

   _____

   Page 418: Who awaits the promise of the rust?

   _____

   _____

3. **Responding to the Selection, page 419.** How does the speaker feel about the season he is describing? Are you able to share his feelings toward this particular season?

   _____

   _____

   _____

   _____

   _____

RESPONDING IN WRITING

1. **Prewriting: Anticipation Poem, page 420.** Think about what you see, hear, smell, taste, and feel as you are waiting. Fill in the sensory detail chart with sensory details of your anticipation.

WHAT I EXPERIENCE WHILE WAITING				
SIGHT	SOUND	TOUCH	TASTE	SMELL

2. **Prewriting: Critical Essay, page 420.** Write a thesis statement that describes the relationship between humans and the environment. Then write an outline of your essay. Use the following form, continue on your own paper and add headings and subheadings as necessary.

Thesis: _____

_____

    I. _____

        A. _____

           1. _____

           2. _____

        B. _____

           1. _____

           2. _____

    II. _____

        A. _____

           1. _____

           2. _____

        B. _____

           1. _____

           2. _____

Selection Worksheet

5.10

"Of Autumn," page 421

READER RESPONSE ACTIVITIES

1. **Reader's Journal, page 422.** Think of some of your favorite details of each of the four seasons—winter, spring, summer, and fall. What events or details are commonly associated with each season? What are some less commonly observed details that are perhaps unique to your perspective?

_____

_____

_____

_____

_____

2. **Guided Reading.** Answer these questions as you read the selection.

   Page 422: What happened to Summer? What could be heard in the garden?

   _____

   _____

   Page 422: What drips from the ivy on the walls? Who is responsible for the massacre of the leaves?

   _____

   _____

3. **Responding to the Selection, page 423:** Have you ever viewed autumn from this perspective? How does this poem make you feel about this season? What might have caused the poet to generate these images of autumn?

   _____

   _____

   _____

   _____

   _____

   _____

   _____

RESPONDING IN WRITING

1. **Prewriting: Season Poem, page 424.** Gather details and images about the season you have chosen. Write the season you have chosen in the center of the cluster chart. In the attached circles write down your ideas about the season. Add more circles if necessary.

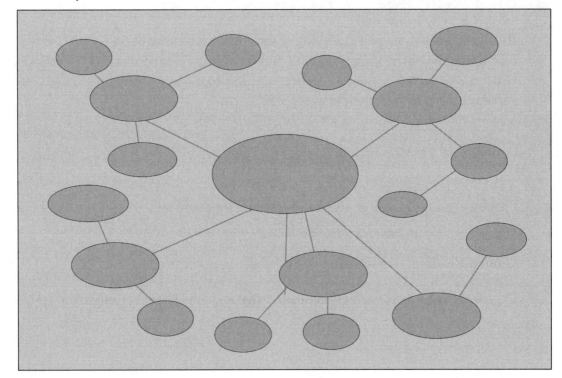

2. **Prewriting: Critical Essay, page 424.** First define tone. Then, in the chart below, identify the tone or tones in "Of Autumn." Note words, phrases, and images that are related to this tone.

Definition:

_____

_____

TONE	WORDS, PHRASES, AND IMAGES

Selection Worksheet

6.1

"The Story of Actaeon," page 436

READER RESPONSE ACTIVITIES

1. **Reader's Journal, page 437.** If you could be something else, such as an animal or a tree, what would you be? On the lines below, describe what you think it would be like to be this thing. Include some of the benefits and drawbacks that you imagine would be part of the experience.

_____

_____

_____

_____

_____

_____

_____

_____

_____

_____

_____

2. **Guided Reading.** Answer these questions as you read the selection.

Page 437: What happens to Actaeon? Does the narrator believe that Actaeon deserves his fate?

_____

_____

Page 437: Where does Diana go to relax after hunting?

_____

_____

Page 438: Where does Actaeon go by mistake?

_____

_____

Page 438: How does Diana feel because Actaeon has seen her? What does she do to him?

_____

_____

_____

Page 438: What changes occur in Actaeon's form?

_____

_____

Page 439: In what way does Actaeon remain unchanged? What choices does he think he has? Why doesn't he like either choice?

_____

_____

Page 440: In what new way do Actaeon's "old companions" behave toward him?

_____

_____

Page 440: What do Actaeon's companions do? In what way does Actaeon respond to his companions?

_____

_____

Page 440: What is Actaeon's fate?

_____

_____

3. **Responding to the Selection, page 441.** The narrator says, "You will find Actaeon guiltless; put the blame / On luck, not crime: what crime is there in error?" Do you, as the narrator expects, find Actaeon guiltless? Do you think that he deserved his fate? How do you feel toward Actaeon? How do you feel toward Diana?

_____

_____

_____

_____

_____

_____

_____

_____

_____

_____

_____

_____

_____

_____

_____

_____

_____

_____

_____

_____

_____

_____

_____

_____

_____

_____

RESPONDING IN WRITING

1. **Prewriting: Transformation Story, page 442.** Decide on the following things before you begin drafting your story.

   Powerful Being: _____

   Motivation: _____

   Description of character who is transformed:

   _____

   _____

   Into what is the character transformed?

   _____

   Consequences of transformation:

   _____

   _____

   _____

2. **Prewriting: Critical Essay, page 442.** In the space below take notes on Ovid's life. You may wish to pay special attention to his relations with people in power and to the punishments he experienced.

Selection Worksheet

"The Lay of the Werewolf," page 444

READER RESPONSE ACTIVITIES

1. **Reader's Journal, page 445.** What were some favorite legends that you heard through stories, poems, or songs as you grew up? What purposes did these tales serve? What elements of these legends or lessons did you find most interesting?

_____

_____

_____

_____

_____

2. **Guided Reading.** Answer these questions as you read the selection.

Page 445: What are the different names for the werewolf? What do werewolves do?

_____

_____

Page 445: What kind of life does the baron lead? To whom is he married? What is his wife's only grief?

_____

_____

Page 446: Why is the baron unwilling to reveal his secret? How does his wife convince him to disclose the secret? What is the secret?

_____

_____

Page 446: How does the wife begin to feel about her husband? Whom does she contact? How does she betray her husband?

_____

_____

Page 446: Why does the baron believe that he can never tell the location of his lair, where he leaves his clothing? What does his wife say to convince him to tell her?

_____

_____

Page 447: What order does the king give to his men and their hounds regarding the beast? Why?

_____

_____

Page 448: How does the king treat Bisclavaret?

_____

_____

Page 448: Why does the former wife of Bisclavaret visit the king? What is Bisclavaret's reaction when she arrives?

_____

_____

Page 448: How does Bisclavaret react to the knight who had taken his wife? What does the household assume from Bisclavaret's actions?

_____

_____

Page 449: What happens to Bisclavaret after he is carried to his chamber? How does the king react to Bisclavaret's change? What does he do for his friend? What happens to Bisclavaret's former wife and her second lord?

_____

_____

Page 449: What does Bisclavaret's former wife tell the people who are questioning her? After hearing the woman's tale, what does the king demand?

_____

_____

3. **Responding to the Selection, page 450.** Why do you think the wife turned against the baron so quickly? Was she justified in her actions? Was the punishment received by the wife and her new husband appropriate? Why, or why not?

_____

_____

_____

_____

_____

_____

_____

_____

_____

_____

_____

_____

_____

_____

_____

_____

_____

_____

_____

_____

_____

_____

_____

RESPONDING IN WRITING

1. **Prewriting: Imaginative Description, page 451.** Complete the sensory detail chart before writing your description.

2.

SENSORY DETAIL CHART				
SIGHT	SOUND	TOUCH	TASTE	SMELL

Prewriting: Critical Essay, page 451. Use the following form to write an outline of your essay. Use your own paper to add more headings and subheadings as necessary.

Name _____ Class _____ Date _____

Thesis: _____

_____

    I. _____

      A. _____

        1. _____

        2. _____

      B. _____

        1. _____

        2. _____

    II. _____

      A. _____

        1. _____

        2. _____

      B. _____

        1. _____

        2. _____

Selection Worksheet

from *The Metamorphosis*, page 454

READER RESPONSE ACTIVITIES

1. **Reader's Journal, page 455.** Do you think sometimes that you work too hard or too little? Do you think your family members work too hard? How important should work be in one's life? How important should fun and relaxation be? What are some ways in which one can try to balance each?

   _____

   _____

   _____

   _____

2. **Guided Reading.** Answer these questions as you read the selection.

   Page 455: Why is this morning unusual for Gregor Samsa?

   _____

   _____

   Page 455: What does Gregor do for a living?

   _____

   _____

   Page 456: What does Gregor dislike about his job?

   _____

   _____

   Page 456: Why must Gregor keep his job, even though he despises it?

   _____

   _____

   Page 456: What panics Gregor most about the situation? What does he fear his boss will do?

   _____

   _____

Page 457: Why does Gregor feel he must get out of bed?

_____

_____

Page 458: What does Gregor expect will happen when he gets out of bed?

_____

_____

Page 458: Why is getting out of bed a difficult maneuver for him?

_____

_____

Page 459: What idea makes Gregor smile?

_____

_____

Page 459: Who is the visitor? What does Gregor lament about the firm? Why does he feel their response to his absence is unreasonable? What does he believe is happening to him?

_____

_____

Page 460: According to Gregor, why might his sister be sobbing?

_____

_____

Page 460: Why does the chief clerk want to speak with Gregor? What does Gregor's mother tell the chief in defense of Gregor?

_____

_____

Page 460: For what does the chief clerk criticize Gregor?

_____

_____

Page 461: What did the chief hint might be a possible explanation for Gregor's disappearance? What, according to the clerk, does not exist in the business world?

_____

_____

Page 461: What does the clerk notice about Gregor's voice? What begins to concern his mother?

_____

_____

Page 463: What is Gregor finally able to do? How?

_____

_____

Page 463: In contrast to how Gregor usually spends his mornings, how does Gregor's father spend his mornings?

_____

_____

Page 463: What is the clerk's and the family's first reaction when Gregor opens the door?

_____

_____

Page 463: What does Gregor tell the clerk about his temporary "incapacity" and his loyalty? What kind of employee does he promise to be? What does he ask the clerk to understand about the life of a traveler?

_____

_____

Page 464: Why, according to Gregor, must the chief clerk not be allowed to leave?

_____

_____

Page 464: How does the chief clerk feel when he sees Gregor? How can you tell?

_____

_____

Page 465: What does Gregor's father wave? Why does he do this?

_____

_____

Page 465: Why is Gregor having trouble returning to his room?

_____

_____

Page 465: Do you think the chief clerk recognizes the creature he sees as Gregor? Explain.

_____

_____

Page 466: What finally helps Gregor through the door? How does it feel to Gregor to be back in his room?

_____

_____

3. **Responding to the Selection, page 467.** If you were a physician, to what would you attribute Gregor's physical condition? If you were a psychiatrist, what would you have to say about Gregor's mental state? What might you say to his family and the chief clerk about their treatment of Gregor?

_____

_____

_____

_____

_____

_____

_____

_____

_____

_____

_____

_____

_____

_____

_____

_____

_____

_____

_____

_____

_____

_____

_____

_____

_____

_____

_____

_____

_____

_____

_____

RESPONDING IN WRITING

1. **Prewriting: Metamorphosis, page 468.** After choosing a form, respond to the following prompts. Use the ideas you list here as you begin to draft your description of a metamorphosis.

Form

_____

My feelings about this form

_____

_____

_____

People's reaction to this form

_____

_____

_____

Difficulties arising from this form

_____

_____

_____

2. Prewriting: Critical Essay, page 468. Begin by answering the following questions. Then after each of your responses, list two or three supporting details.

1. How much of Gregor's life is devoted to work?

_____

Supporting Details

_____

_____

2. How seriously does he take his work?

_____

Supporting Details

_____

_____

3. Does Gregor work for himself, or for the good of others?

_____

Supporting Details

_____

_____

4. How much respect does Gregor get from the people with whom he works?

_____

Supporting Details

_____

_____

Selection Worksheet

"Lot's Wife," page 470

READER RESPONSE ACTIVITIES

1. **Reader's Journal, page 471.** How would you feel if you were forced to leave your home? Have you ever had to leave a place that was filled with happy memories and feelings of security for you? If yes, describe these feelings. If no, write about what you imagine these feelings would be like.

   _____

   _____

   _____

   _____

   _____

2. **Guided Reading.** Answer these questions as you read the selection.

   Page 471: Whom did Lot follow? What did his wife's grief for her lost home tell her to do?

   _____

   _____

   Page 471: What happened to Lot's wife when she looked back?

   _____

   _____

   Page 471: Why will this woman "not be forgot"? For what did she give up her life?

   _____

   _____

3. **Responding to the Selection, page 472.** Why do you suppose Lot's wife looked back? If you were Lot's wife, might you have done the same thing that she did? Why, or why not?

   _____

   _____

   _____

   _____

_____

_____

_____

RESPONDING IN WRITING

1. **Prewriting: Monologue, page 473.** Think about your character. In the space below, do a focused freewrite about your character's actions, feelings, and motivations.

_____

_____

_____

_____

_____

_____

_____

_____

2. **Prewriting: Critical Essay, page 473.** Begin by answering the following questions. Then after each of your responses, list two or three supporting details.

1. What is Lot's wife feeling?

_____

Supporting Details

_____

_____

2. What is Lot's wife remembering?

_____

Supporting Details

_____

_____

3. Is the speaker sympathetic to Lot's wife?

_____

Supporting Details

_____

_____

Selection Worksheet

6.5

"The Fifth Story," page 474

READER RESPONSE ACTIVITIES

1. **Reader's Journal, page 475.** On the lines below, describe some decisions that have been easy for you to make and some that have required careful thought. Provide reasons why the latter are more difficult than the former.

_____

_____

_____

_____

_____

_____

_____

_____

2. **Guided Reading.** Answer these questions as you read the selection.

Page 475: What are the different story titles the narrator considers? At least how many stories does the narrator say will be told?

_____

_____

Page 475: How does the narrator begin to feel about the cockroaches? What "guides" the narrator as she prepares the poison?

_____

_____

Page 475: What is the recipe for killing cockroaches? What did the mixture do to the creatures?

_____

_____

Page 476: What has the poison done to the cockroaches? What does the narrator see when she awakens?

_____

_____

Page 477: To what does the narrator compare the cockroaches? What does the narrator imagine the cockroaches thinking and doing just before they die?

_____

_____

Page 477: What choice does the narrator feel she has? What choice does she end up making?

_____

_____

Page 477: What does the narrator say she watches from her "frigid height as a human being"?

_____

_____

3. **Responding to the Selection, page 478.** Can you identify with the narrator's continually changing feelings about the action of ridding her apartment of cockroaches? Why, or why not? What other stories might be possible for her?

_____

_____

_____

_____

_____

_____

_____

_____

_____

_____

_____

_____

_____

_____

_____

_____

_____

_____

_____

_____

_____

_____

_____

_____

_____

_____

RESPONDING IN WRITING

1. **Prewriting: Three Stories in One, page 479.** In the first column of the chart below, write a detached version of the situation you have chosen by breaking the activity into steps. Write the emotional response that will characterize one of the other stories at the top of each of the other columns. Then fill each column with reactions, feelings, and explanations that correspond to different parts of the process.

DETACHED VERSION	EMOTIONAL RESPONSE A EMOTION _____	EMOTIONAL RESPONSE B EMOTION _____

2. **Prewriting: Critical Essay, page 480.** Make a chart of the narrator's attitude toward the cockroaches. In the first column, list in order the attitudes the narrator displays. In the second column, list one or more words or phrases that show this attitude.

ATTITUDE	WORDS AND PHRASES
Attitude 1: _____ _____	_____ _____ _____ _____ _____ _____
Attitude 2: _____ _____	_____ _____ _____ _____ _____ _____
Attitude 3: _____ _____	_____ _____ _____ _____ _____ _____

Selection Worksheet

6.6

"The Youngest Doll," page 481

READER RESPONSE ACTIVITIES

1. **Reader's Journal, page 482.** Have you ever been in a situation in which you were judged, not on your personal characteristics or on any quality you could control, but on circumstances beyond your influence, such as your heritage, sex, or family background? What happened? What did it feel like to be unable to control the way in which you were perceived? In what way did this situation affect your behavior during that particular moment?

_____

_____

_____

_____

_____

_____

2. **Guided Reading.** Answer these questions as you read the selection.

Page 482: In what way did the incident with the prawn change the aunt's life?

_____

_____

Page 482: What has happened to the aunt?

_____

_____

Page 482: What is the financial situation of this family? To what is their wealthy past compared?

_____

_____

Page 483: What does the aunt spend all day doing? When are the only times she will wake from her stupor?

_____

_____

Page 483: In what way does the aunt use the dolls to mark the way the girls are growing up?

_____

_____

Page 484: Why does the aunt put the dolls' glass eyes in the stream?

_____

_____

Page 484: What does the aunt do when one of the daughters gets married? What does she tell the groom?

_____

_____

Page 485: How does the young doctor treat his wife? What does she begin to suspect?

_____

_____

Page 485: What does the doctor's son realize about the prawn in the aunt's leg? What explanation does the doctor provide for his actions?

_____

_____

Page 485: What confirms the youngest daughter's suspicions?

_____

_____

Page 485: Why does the doctor want to know where the doll is?

_____

_____

Page 486: What do visitors notice about the youngest daughter? What do the visitors feel an urge to do?

_____

_____

Page 486: What does the youngest daughter now do? What effect has her presence had on her husband's business?

_____

_____

Page 486: What word is used to describe the youngest daughter? What comes from her eyes? Into what has the youngest daughter been transformed?

_____

_____

3. **Responding to the Selection, page 487.** What is your reaction to this story? What images from this story particularly surprised or shocked you? If you were asked to review this story for a classmate, what would you say?

_____

_____

_____

_____

_____

_____

_____

_____

_____

_____

_____

_____

_____

_____

_____

_____

_____

RESPONDING IN WRITING

1. **Prewriting: Personal Essay, page 488.** After choosing a situation, freewrite about your emotional reactions to this situation. Then review your freewrite for vivid images that might be used to describe your experience.

_____

_____

_____

_____

_____

_____

_____

_____

_____

_____

_____

_____

_____

_____

_____

_____

_____

_____

2. **Prewriting: Critical Essay, page 489.** Use the following form to write an outline of your essay. First write your thesis. Then for the main topics, identify techniques used by the author. Under each main idea, list supporting details from the story. Use your own paper to add more headings and subheadings as necessary.

Thesis: _____

_____

 I. _____

   A. _____

      1. _____

      2. _____

   B. _____

      1. _____

      2. _____

 II. _____

   A. _____

      1. _____

      2. _____

   B. _____

      1. _____

      2. _____

Selection Worksheet

from *The Epic of Gilgamesh*, page 502

READER RESPONSE ACTIVITIES

1. **Reader's Journal, page 503.** On the lines below, respond to the following questions: Do you think that people should be able to live forever? If you had the opportunity to drink from the fountain of youth and live forever would you take it? Why, or why not? What might be the advantages and disadvantages of living for hundreds or thousands of years?

_____

_____

_____

_____

_____

_____

_____

_____

2. **Guided Reading.** Answer these questions as you read the selection.

   Page 504: According to the narrator, who originally wrote *The Epic of Gilgamesh*?

   _____

   _____

   Page 504: In what ways is Gilgamesh unlike an ordinary mortal?

   _____

   _____

   Page 504: What does Enkidu dream? Why does Anu say that Enkidu must die? Does Enkidu believe that this dream is just an idle imagining, or does he believe it will come to pass?

   _____

   _____

   Page 505: How does Enkidu feel about the fact that he must die?

   _____

   _____

Page 506: Where does the "awful being" bring Enkidu in his dream?

_____

_____

Page 506: What is the underworld like? In what way is death an equalizing force?

_____

_____

Page 506: What shames Enkidu about his death? How had he hoped to die?

_____

_____

Page 506: In what way would you characterize Gilgamesh's reaction to Enkidu's death?

_____

_____

Page 507: What makes Gilgamesh finally give up Enkidu to the earth?

_____

_____

Page 507: What does Utnapishtim's answer mean?

_____

_____

Page 507: Why can't Gilgamesh rest? What does he hope to do?

_____

_____

Page 508: What surprises Gilgamesh about Utnapishtim? Why does this surprise him?

_____

_____

Page 508: What does Ea tell Utnapishtim to say to the people of Shurrupak? Why does Ea tell Utnapishtim to lie?

_____

_____

Page 508: Why do the gods want to exterminate humankind? Who warns Utnapishtim and why?

_____

_____

Page 508: What does Ea tell Utnapishtim to do?

_____

_____

Page 509: In what way do the gods react to the flood? What does Ishtar regret?

_____

_____

Page 510: What has happened to the world?

_____

_____

Page 510: According to Ea, why was Enlil's punishment "senseless"?

_____

_____

Page 510: What does Utnapishtim do when he sees that the waters have retreated? To what does Utnapishtim compare the gods? Is this a flattering comparison?

_____

_____

Page 511: What is the first thing that Gilgamesh says when he awakens? In what way does this prove true Utnapishtim's belief about humanity?

_____

_____

Page 511: What does Enlil do in response to Ea's criticism of his actions?

_____

_____

Page 511: What does Utnapishtim ask Gilgamesh? What contest does Utnapishtim suggest to Gilgamesh? What does Gilgamesh do immediately?

_____

_____

Page 511: What does Utnapishtim say about human beings? What does he tell his wife to do? Why?

_____

_____

Page 512: What happens to the plant? What occurrence in the natural world does this story explain?

_____

_____

Page 512: What does Utnapishtim "give" Gilgamesh for a gift?

_____

_____

Page 512: In what way does Gilgamesh achieve a limited type of immortality?

_____

_____

3. **Responding to the Selection, page 513.** What does the word _hero_ mean to you? Did Gilgamesh seem heroic to you? Why, or why not? Discuss with your classmates why you would or would not classify Gilgamesh as a hero.

_____

_____

_____

_____

_____

_____

_____

_____

_____

_____

_____

_____

_____

_____

_____

_____

_____

_____

_____

_____

_____

_____

_____

_____

_____

_____

RESPONDING IN WRITING

1. **Prewriting: Heroic Quest, page 514.** On your own paper, answer the following questions: Is your hero male or female? Is your hero a historical figure, a figure from popular culture or literature, or your own imaginative creation? What heroic qualities does your hero possess? What does he or she look like? How does he or she sound? What does your hero value? For what might your hero undertake a quest? Then complete the following story map in which you outline the plot of your heroic quest.

Story Map

Setting and Mood

Time _____

_____

Place _____

Mood _____

_____

Major characters

_____

_____

Conflict ___ internal ___ external

_____

Conflict ___ internal ___ external

_____

Conflict ___ internal ___ external

_____

Plot
Inciting incident _____

Climax _____

Resolution _____

Themes _____

2. **Prewriting: Critical Essay, page 515.** On the lines below, freewrite about the following questions before developing your thesis: What is Gilgamesh like at the beginning of the epic? What is he like at the epic's end? What does Gilgamesh lose on his quest? What does he gain? Why might it sometimes be necessary to lose something in order to gain something? Is what Gilgamesh gains worth its cost?

_____

_____

_____

_____

_____

_____

_____

_____

_____

_____

_____

_____

_____

_____

_____

_____

_____

_____

_____

_____

_____

Selection Worksheet

7.2

from Genesis, page 518

READER RESPONSE ACTIVITIES

1. **Reader's Journal, page 519.** Describe your idea of paradise. What would it be like to live there? How would you feel upon being forced to leave?

   _____

   _____

   _____

   _____

2. **Guided Reading.** Answer these questions as you read the selection.

   Page 519: What is the earth like before the beginning of creation?

   _____

   _____

   Page 519: In what way does God create light?

   _____

   _____

   Page 520: What life forms are created first? In what way are these life forms created?

   _____

   _____

   Page 520: In what way are humans created? What blessing does God give to humans?

   _____

   _____

   Page 521: In what way is man created?

   _____

   _____

   Page 521: What does God cause to grow in Eden?

   _____

   _____

Page 521: What are God's instructions to the man?

_____

_____

Page 522: What effect does tasting the fruit from the tree of knowledge of good and evil have on Adam and Eve?

_____

_____

Page 522: In what way is the serpent subtle?

_____

_____

Page 523: In what different ways do Cain and Abel make their livelihoods?

_____

_____

Page 523: What effect does Adam and Eve's fall have on the future of humankind?

_____

_____

Page 523: How does Cain feel toward Abel and why?

_____

_____

Page 523: Why does God expel Adam and Eve from Eden?

_____

_____

Page 524: Why is Noah spared from the flood?

_____

_____

Page 524: What is Cain's punishment for spilling his brother's blood?

_____

_____

Page 524: What does God tell Noah to do?

_____

_____

Page 524: Why does God repent making humans?

_____

_____

Page 525: What does God ask Noah to bring with him? Why does God ask Noah to bring these things?

_____

_____

Page 525: When will God send the flood? How long will the flood last? What is the purpose of the flood?

_____

_____

Page 526: What effect does the flood have on the earth?

_____

_____

Page 527: For how long was the earth covered by the waters?

_____

_____

Page 527: What is the first thing that Noah does once he is upon dry land?

_____

_____

Page 527: What does the Lord decide in His heart? Why does He make this decision?

_____

_____

Page 527: What sign reveals that the waters have abated?

_____

_____

Page 528: What is God's covenant with Noah?

_____

_____

3. **Responding to the Selection, page 529.** Which Biblical story, the creation or the flood, evoked the strongest emotional reaction in you? Discuss your reaction to this story with your classmates. Do you think this story produced the same reaction in an ancient Hebrew audience? Why, or why not?

_____

_____

_____

_____

RESPONDING IN WRITING

1. **Prewriting: Journal Entry, page 530.** Do two focused freewrites. On your own paper, freewrite about the situation in which your character finds himself or herself. Then freewrite about your character's feelings or reactions to the situation.

2. **Prewriting: Critical Essay, page 530.** Use the chart below to compare elements of the Biblical account of the flood with that in *The Epic of Gilgamesh*.

	GENESIS	GILGAMESH
Why God/gods cause flood		
Fate of survivor		
Context in which flood story is told		

Selection Worksheet

7.3

from the *Popol Vuh*, page 532

READER RESPONSE ACTIVITIES

1. **Reader's Journal, page 533.** Think about the questions you have about the existence of the world around you. Choose one question and write a possible explanation for it.

   _____

   _____

   _____

   _____

   _____

   _____

   _____

   _____

2. **Guided Reading.** Answer these questions as you read the selection.

   Page 533: What could the four new people do?

   _____

   _____

   Page 533: In what way were the four "truly gifted"?

   _____

   _____

   Page 534: In what way do the creators mar their creations?

   _____

   _____

   Page 534: About what are the creator gods worried?

   _____

   _____

   Page 535: Why were the new people crying?

   _____

   _____

3. **Responding to the Selection, page 536.** What ideas or beliefs expressed in this myth seemed strange or unfamiliar to you? Which of your beliefs might seem strange to a person from the ancient Mayan culture?

_____

_____

_____

_____

_____

_____

_____

_____

_____

_____

_____

_____

_____

_____

_____

_____

_____

_____

_____

_____

_____

_____

_____

_____

RESPONDING IN WRITING

1. **Prewriting: Description, page 537.** To gather details about the world long ago, fill in the sensory detail chart with images about the world as you imagine it was.

THE WORLD LONG AGO				
SIGHT	SOUND	TOUCH	TASTE	SMELL

2. **Prewriting: Critical Essay, page 537.** Use the Venn diagram below to collect information for your comparison and contrast essay.

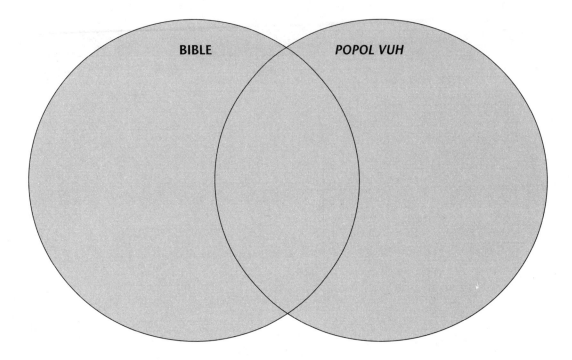

Selection Worksheet

"The Five Worlds and Their Suns," page 538

READER RESPONSE ACTIVITIES

1. **Reader's Journal, page 539.** On the lines below, write about a time in your life when you had to make a sacrifice. Maybe you had to give up something you enjoyed to help someone else, or perhaps you had to sacrifice a short-term desire to achieve a long-term goal. Was it difficult to make this sacrifice? How did you feel about doing so?

_____

_____

_____

_____

_____

_____

_____

_____

_____

_____

_____

_____

_____

_____

_____

_____

_____

2. **Guided Reading.** Answer these questions as you read the selection.

   Page 539: Under what condition will the human couple survive the flood?

   _____

   _____

   Page 539: What explanation is offered for the origin of apes?

   _____

   _____

Page 539: Why do the gods become enraged with the couple?

_____

_____

Page 539: What flaw did people of the fourth world have?

_____

_____

Page 540: How do the other gods feel about Nanautzin? What do the gods promise Nanautzin?

_____

_____

Page 540: In what way do the offerings of the wealthy god and of Nanautzin differ?

_____

_____

Page 541: In what way does the behavior of the two gods differ?

_____

_____

3. **Responding to the Selection, page 542**. Do you admire Nanautzin? Why, or why not? What is your opinion of the wealthy god? Explain.

_____

_____

_____

_____

_____

_____

_____

_____

_____

_____

_____

_____

_____

_____

_____

_____

_____

_____

_____

_____

_____

_____

_____

_____

_____

_____

_____

_____

_____

_____

_____

_____

RESPONDING IN WRITING

1. **Prewriting: Praise Poem, page 543.** Before you begin to draft your praise poem, answer the following questions:

   What did the person do for you?

   _____

   Why was this a sacrifice for the person?

   _____

   In what way did the sacrifice help you?

   _____

   Was the sacrifice characteristic of the person, or was it surprising? Explain.

   _____

   What other praiseworthy things has this person done?

   _____

2. **Prewriting: Critical Essay, page 543.** Use the Venn diagram below to collect information for your comparison and contrast essay. As you fill in the chart, pay special attention to the way in which the relationship between humans and their environment and/or the gods is depicted in each myth.

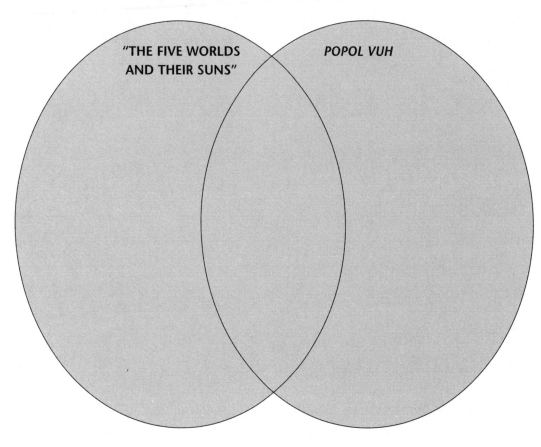

Selection Worksheet

from the *Tao Te Ching*, page 544

READER RESPONSE ACTIVITIES

1. **Reader's Journal, page 545.** Answer the following question on the lines below: Do you believe that people have become too caught up in earthly distractions, such as money, cars, clothing, television, and careers? Explain, drawing from examples you see in your own life and the lives of others.

_____

_____

_____

_____

_____

_____

_____

_____

_____

_____

2. **Guided Reading.** Answer these questions as you read the selection.

   Page 545: What is not the eternal Tao? What is the beginning of heaven and earth?

   _____

   _____

   Page 545: Why might one need to be "desireless" to understand the mystery?

   _____

   _____

   Page 545: Why is one able to see beauty as beauty? Why is one able to know good?

   _____

   _____

   Page 546: In what way is the universe perfectly balanced, according to Lao-tzu?

   _____

   _____

Page 546: Why is the highest good like water?

_____

_____

Page 546: When in action, of what should one be aware?

_____

_____

Page 546: What will happen if one tries to change or to hold the universe?

_____

_____

3. **Responding to the Selection, page 547.** What do you consider most interesting about the teachings of Lao-tzu? If you were to meet Lao-tzu, what might you ask him or tell him about his work?

_____

_____

_____

_____

_____

_____

_____

_____

_____

_____

_____

_____

_____

_____

_____

_____

_____

_____

Name _____ Class _____ Date _____

_____

_____

_____

_____

_____

_____

_____

_____

_____

_____

RESPONDING IN WRITING

1. **Prewriting: Paradoxical Scene, page 549.** You might begin by brainstorming a list of opposites, for example: *fail* and *succeed*, *win* and *lose*, *give* and *take*. Then freewrite about how one or more of these pairs of opposites could figure in a paradoxical situation.

2. **Prewriting: Critical Essay, page 549.** After choosing one of Lao-tzu's teachings as your subject, list examples from your own life that support your praise or criticism of this teaching. In the space below, organize your ideas in a rough outline.

Selection Worksheet

from the *Analects*, page 550

READER RESPONSE ACTIVITIES

1. **Reader's Journal, page 551.** In your opinion, what makes a person wise? On the lines below, answer the above question, and then list two or three people whom you consider to be wise. These people can be teachers, religious leaders, family members, or friends. Explain why you consider these people to be wise.

   _____

   _____

   _____

   _____

2. **Guided Reading.** Answer these questions as you read the selection.

   Page 551: What is more important than being understood?

   _____

   _____

   Page 551: What does the disciple of Confucius ask himself every day? Who is the "Master" to whom the disciple Zeng Zi refers?

   _____

   _____

   Page 551: According to Confucius, in what way should a young man treat his parents? his elders?

   _____

   _____

   Page 552: Why does Confucius learn from another person's merits as well as from his or her shortcomings?

   _____

   _____

   Page 552: What would Confucius say to describe himself to a stranger?

   _____

   _____

3. **Responding to the Selection, page 553.** Which two teachings did you find most interesting and applicable to your own life? Why did these teachings appeal to you?

_____

_____

_____

_____

_____

RESPONDING IN WRITING

1. **Prewriting: Aphorisms, page 554.** First review your responses to the Reader's Journal activity on page 551 of your textbook. Then freewrite about rules of conduct for life, politics, leadership, and relationships. Use ideas from your freewrite to create your aphorisms.

_____

_____

_____

_____

_____

_____

_____

2. **Prewriting: Critical Essay, page 554.** After reviewing the information about Confucius and Lao-tzu and reviewing the ideas they present in their works, complete the Venn diagram below. Use the information you gather to organize and draft your essay.

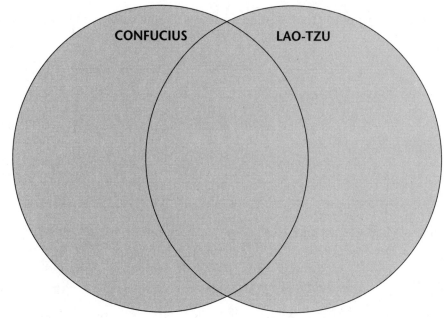

Selection Worksheet

from "Creation Hymn," page 556

READER RESPONSE ACTIVITIES

1. **Reader's Journal, page 557.** Think of a time when you had a question about the world that remained unanswered. Maybe you wondered what our planet looked like long ago, or perhaps you wondered what you would discover if you could dive to the bottom of the deepest ocean. Write about your questions in your journal.

_____

_____

_____

_____

_____

_____

_____

2. **Guided Reading.** Answer these questions as you read the selection.

   Page 557: Does the speaker in this hymn know the answers to his or her questions? Does anyone know, according to the speaker?

   _____

   _____

3. **Responding to the Selection, page 558.** What do you think about the questions posed in "The Creation Hymn"? Do questions such as these interest you? Why, or why not?

   _____

   _____

   _____

   _____

   _____

   _____

   _____

   _____

   _____

RESPONDING IN WRITING

1. **Prewriting: Descriptive Paragraph, page 559.** Take a few minutes to visualize the world before the creation. Then fill in the sensory detail chart with images of this world. You may also wish to describe this world by showing what is missing. In that case, identify images that might suggest many of the things that are missing from the world. For example: There is no sound. No birds sing, no babies cry, no thunder rumbles.

THE WORLD BEFORE CREATION				
SIGHT	SOUND	TOUCH	TASTE	SMELL

2. **Prewriting: Critical Essay, page 559.** As you research the three gods, fill in the chart below. As you identify a characteristic of one god, place it in the chart. Then, in the other columns write in a similar element related to the other gods.

INDRA	ZEUS	THOR

Selection Worksheet

from the *Ramayana*, page 560

READER RESPONSE ACTIVITIES

1. **Reader's Journal, page 561.** Who are your own heroes? What qualities do you most admire in these people? Write responses to these questions in your journal.

_____

_____

_____

_____

_____

_____

_____

_____

_____

_____

2. **Guided Reading.** Answer these questions as you read the selection.

Page 561: How does Valmiki respond to the killing of the bird? What happens to the hunter as a result?

_____

_____

Page 562: What evil deeds does Ravana do?

_____

_____

Page 562: According to Brahma, what gave birth to the world's first verse? What does Brahma ask Valmiki to do?

_____

_____

Page 562: How does Ravana violate the Hindu law of hospitality toward guests and the universal rule of proper conduct toward a messenger, emissary, or diplomat?

_____

_____

Page 563: What universal law is embodied in the person of the god Vishnu?

_____

_____

Page 563: What physical characteristics show Vishnu to be more than an ordinary being?

_____

_____

Page 563: Why does Vishnu refuse to permit Indra to wage war again on Ravana?

_____

_____

Page 563: What does Indra ask Vishnu to do?

_____

_____

Page 564: What do Rama and Lakshmana want to see? Who will receive the bow and under what circumstances?

_____

_____

Page 565: What unusual circumstances are involved in Sita's birth?

_____

_____

Page 565: What has happened to Sita?

_____

_____

Page 565: Is Rama one to remember injuries and to hold grudges? How does Rama show that he respects individual differences?

_____

_____

Page 565: What does Rama find surprisingly easy? Why might this be easy for him?

_____

_____

Page 565: What abilities show Rama to be both strong and gentle? Under what circumstances, according to the *Ramayana*, does a person's anger "go for nothing"?

⎯⎯⎯⎯⎯⎯⎯⎯⎯⎯⎯⎯⎯⎯⎯⎯⎯⎯⎯⎯⎯⎯⎯⎯⎯⎯⎯⎯⎯⎯⎯⎯⎯⎯

⎯⎯⎯⎯⎯⎯⎯⎯⎯⎯⎯⎯⎯⎯⎯⎯⎯⎯⎯⎯⎯⎯⎯⎯⎯⎯⎯⎯⎯⎯⎯⎯⎯⎯

Page 566: What disguise does Ravana use?

⎯⎯⎯⎯⎯⎯⎯⎯⎯⎯⎯⎯⎯⎯⎯⎯⎯⎯⎯⎯⎯⎯⎯⎯⎯⎯⎯⎯⎯⎯⎯⎯⎯⎯

⎯⎯⎯⎯⎯⎯⎯⎯⎯⎯⎯⎯⎯⎯⎯⎯⎯⎯⎯⎯⎯⎯⎯⎯⎯⎯⎯⎯⎯⎯⎯⎯⎯⎯

Page 567: How does Sita respond to Ravana's flattery and promises?

⎯⎯⎯⎯⎯⎯⎯⎯⎯⎯⎯⎯⎯⎯⎯⎯⎯⎯⎯⎯⎯⎯⎯⎯⎯⎯⎯⎯⎯⎯⎯⎯⎯⎯

⎯⎯⎯⎯⎯⎯⎯⎯⎯⎯⎯⎯⎯⎯⎯⎯⎯⎯⎯⎯⎯⎯⎯⎯⎯⎯⎯⎯⎯⎯⎯⎯⎯⎯

Page 567: Why does Ravana suddenly become angry and show his true form?

⎯⎯⎯⎯⎯⎯⎯⎯⎯⎯⎯⎯⎯⎯⎯⎯⎯⎯⎯⎯⎯⎯⎯⎯⎯⎯⎯⎯⎯⎯⎯⎯⎯⎯

⎯⎯⎯⎯⎯⎯⎯⎯⎯⎯⎯⎯⎯⎯⎯⎯⎯⎯⎯⎯⎯⎯⎯⎯⎯⎯⎯⎯⎯⎯⎯⎯⎯⎯

Page 567: What happens to Sita?

⎯⎯⎯⎯⎯⎯⎯⎯⎯⎯⎯⎯⎯⎯⎯⎯⎯⎯⎯⎯⎯⎯⎯⎯⎯⎯⎯⎯⎯⎯⎯⎯⎯⎯

⎯⎯⎯⎯⎯⎯⎯⎯⎯⎯⎯⎯⎯⎯⎯⎯⎯⎯⎯⎯⎯⎯⎯⎯⎯⎯⎯⎯⎯⎯⎯⎯⎯⎯

Page 568: How does Hanuman kill the demon Sinhika?

⎯⎯⎯⎯⎯⎯⎯⎯⎯⎯⎯⎯⎯⎯⎯⎯⎯⎯⎯⎯⎯⎯⎯⎯⎯⎯⎯⎯⎯⎯⎯⎯⎯⎯

⎯⎯⎯⎯⎯⎯⎯⎯⎯⎯⎯⎯⎯⎯⎯⎯⎯⎯⎯⎯⎯⎯⎯⎯⎯⎯⎯⎯⎯⎯⎯⎯⎯⎯

Page 568: What is exceptional about Hanuman's leap?

⎯⎯⎯⎯⎯⎯⎯⎯⎯⎯⎯⎯⎯⎯⎯⎯⎯⎯⎯⎯⎯⎯⎯⎯⎯⎯⎯⎯⎯⎯⎯⎯⎯⎯

⎯⎯⎯⎯⎯⎯⎯⎯⎯⎯⎯⎯⎯⎯⎯⎯⎯⎯⎯⎯⎯⎯⎯⎯⎯⎯⎯⎯⎯⎯⎯⎯⎯⎯

Page 569: What magical power does Ravana's mace have?

⎯⎯⎯⎯⎯⎯⎯⎯⎯⎯⎯⎯⎯⎯⎯⎯⎯⎯⎯⎯⎯⎯⎯⎯⎯⎯⎯⎯⎯⎯⎯⎯⎯⎯

⎯⎯⎯⎯⎯⎯⎯⎯⎯⎯⎯⎯⎯⎯⎯⎯⎯⎯⎯⎯⎯⎯⎯⎯⎯⎯⎯⎯⎯⎯⎯⎯⎯⎯

Page 570: How does the charioteer Matali save Rama's life?

⎯⎯⎯⎯⎯⎯⎯⎯⎯⎯⎯⎯⎯⎯⎯⎯⎯⎯⎯⎯⎯⎯⎯⎯⎯⎯⎯⎯⎯⎯⎯⎯⎯⎯

⎯⎯⎯⎯⎯⎯⎯⎯⎯⎯⎯⎯⎯⎯⎯⎯⎯⎯⎯⎯⎯⎯⎯⎯⎯⎯⎯⎯⎯⎯⎯⎯⎯⎯

Page 571: How does Ravana die?

⎯⎯⎯⎯⎯⎯⎯⎯⎯⎯⎯⎯⎯⎯⎯⎯⎯⎯⎯⎯⎯⎯⎯⎯⎯⎯⎯⎯⎯⎯⎯⎯⎯⎯

⎯⎯⎯⎯⎯⎯⎯⎯⎯⎯⎯⎯⎯⎯⎯⎯⎯⎯⎯⎯⎯⎯⎯⎯⎯⎯⎯⎯⎯⎯⎯⎯⎯⎯

Page 571: What shape does Ravana assume? Why does Rama hesitate?

_____

_____

Page 572: What did Ravana know about Rama all along?

_____

_____

3. **Responding to the Selection, page 573.** Does Rama fit your idea of a hero? Why, or why not?

_____

_____

_____

_____

_____

_____

_____

_____

_____

_____

_____

_____

_____

_____

_____

_____

_____

_____

_____

_____

RESPONDING IN WRITING

1. **Prewriting: Description, page 574.** Fill in the following sensory detail chart with descriptive images of your character and his, her, or its actions.

CHARACTER DESCRIPTION
<u>SIGHT</u>
<u>SOUND</u>
<u>TOUCH</u>
<u>TASTE</u>
<u>SMELL</u>

2. **Prewriting: Critical Essay, page 574.** Use the analysis chart below to list the elements of the allegory presented in the *Ramayana* and to explain how each element is related to the whole.

ANALYSIS OF THE RAMAYANA	
ELEMENT	**RELATIONSHIP TO WHOLE**

Selection Worksheet

from the *Sunjata*, page 575

READER RESPONSE ACTIVITIES

1. **Reader's Journal, page 576.** Do you believe in fate or destiny? Have you ever felt that something occurred because it was destined to be? If so, describe this occurrence as well as what led you to feel that the occurrence was predetermined. If not, explain why you do not believe in fate or destiny.

_____

_____

_____

_____

_____

_____

_____

_____

_____

_____

_____

_____

2. **Guided Reading.** Answer these questions as you read the selection.

   Page 576: What special powers does the beast possess?

   _____

   _____

   Page 576: Why does Sunjata want to kill the beast?

   _____

   _____

   Page 577: Who is the beast? How does Sogolon Kedju say it can be killed?

   _____

   _____

Page 577: How does Sunjata treat the old man? What does the old man say Sunjata will reap?

_____

_____

Page 578: Why do you think Sunjata conceals his identity?

_____

_____

Page 579: What does the old woman reveal? What does she tell Sunjata he must do?

_____

_____

Page 579: How will the beast die? What role is Sunjata to play in this death?

_____

_____

3. **Responding to the Selection, page 580.** Did the events described in the *Sunjata* seem realistic to you? Why, or why not? What did you think of the old woman's decision to tell Sunjata how to kill her? Did this seem realistic? Why, or why not? Why might realism not have been a priority in this epic?

_____

_____

_____

_____

_____

_____

_____

_____

_____

_____

_____

_____

_____

_____

_____

_____

_____

_____

_____

_____

_____

RESPONDING IN WRITING

1. **Prewriting: Character Sketch, page 582.** Before you draft your character sketch, answer the following questions:

   What does your hero look like?

   _____

   _____

   _____

   What does your hero wear?

   _____

   _____

   What does his or her voice sound like?

   _____

   _____

   What actions make this person remarkable?

   _____

   _____

   _____

2. **Prewriting: Critical Essay, page 582.** Carefully reread the selection, keeping in mind the following questions: To what extent are the events that occur in the characters' lives the result of fate? What impact does the belief in predestination have on the actions of the characters? Would the outcome of this adventure have been different if Sunjata had been able to separate himself from his destiny and behave differently, or did Sunjata's character determine his actions and, hence, his fate? Take notes in response to these questions as your read. Then organize your ideas in a rough outline in the space below.

_____

_____

_____

_____

_____

_____

_____

_____

_____

_____

_____

_____

_____

_____

_____

_____

_____

_____

_____

_____

_____

Selection Worksheet

from the *Iliad* page 592

READER RESPONSE ACTIVITIES

1. **Reader's Journal, page 594.** What images does the word *revenge* bring to your mind? What emotions do you think a person seeking revenge feels? Is vengeance always the best way to deal with people who have wronged you? Why, or why not?

_____

_____

_____

_____

_____

_____

_____

_____

_____

_____

_____

_____

_____

_____

_____

_____

_____

2. **Guided Reading.** Answer these questions as you read the selection.

   Page 596: Why does Hector feel that he must fight Achilles? Why does he feel shame? Whom does he not want to face unless he challenges Achilles alone?

   _____

   _____

   Page 596: What is Hector tempted to do?

   _____

   _____

Page 596: Why does Hector decide not to try to reason with Achilles? What does he believe would happen if he tried to do this?

_____

_____

Page 597: What does Hector do when he sees Achilles approaching? What does Achilles do? To what is this encounter compared?

_____

_____

Page 598: Why does Zeus feel grief for Hector? What must the gods decide?

_____

_____

Page 598: How does Athena say the other gods will respond if Zeus spares Hector?

_____

_____

Page 599: What allowed Hector to flee from death for so long?

_____

_____

Page 599: What happens when Zeus takes out the sacred golden scales? What does Athena promise Achilles? What must she persuade Hector to do?

_____

_____

Page 600: How does Athena try to deceive Hector into fighting Achilles "face-to-face"?

_____

_____

Page 600: What does Hector swear?

_____

_____

Page 600: Why won't Achilles swear the same oath? To what does he compare himself and Hector?

_____

_____

Page 601: What happens when Achilles throws a spear at Hector? What does Athena do?

_____

_____

Page 602: According to Hector, what would Achilles's death mean for the Trojans?

_____

_____

Page 602: When does Hector realize that Athena had tricked him? What is his attitude toward his inevitable death? What does he do in his attempt to die with glory?

_____

_____

Page 603: Whose armor is Hector wearing? What vulnerability does Achilles detect?

_____

_____

Page 603: What does Achilles say to taunt Hector?

_____

_____

Page 603: What does Hector fear might happen to his body after he is dead? What last request does he make of Achilles?

_____

_____

Page 604: Is Achilles sympathetic to Hector's request? According to Achilles, what will happen to Hector's body?

_____

_____

Page 605: Of what does Hector warn Achilles?

_____

_____

Page 605: What attitude does Achilles express toward his own death?

_____

_____

Page 605: What do Achilles and his men do to Hector's body?

_____

_____

Page 605: What does Achilles wonder about the Trojans? What does he then remember about Patroclus? What does he vow?

_____

_____

Page 606: What "outrage" upon Hector's dead body does Achilles commit?

_____

_____

3. **Responding to the Selection, page 606.** How would Achilles describe Hector and his actions? How would Hector's parents and the people of Troy describe Achilles? For whom do you feel the most sympathy and understanding?

_____

_____

_____

_____

_____

_____

_____

_____

_____

_____

_____

_____

_____

_____

_____

_____

_____

_____

RESPONDING IN WRITING

1. **Prewriting: Parody, page 608.** First identify an everyday conflict. In the space below, freewrite a description of it in your own terms. Then transform the words, emotions, and actions from this description into Homeric style.

_____

_____

_____

_____

_____

_____

_____

_____

_____

_____

_____

_____

_____

_____

_____

_____

_____

_____

_____

_____

_____

_____

_____

_____

_____

_____

2. **Prewriting: Critical Essay, page 608.** In the space below, answer the following questions. Use your responses to these questions as you formulate a thesis and draft your essay.

What characteristics of Achilles are presented?

_____

What does Homer want the reader to understand about the character of Achilles in his dealings with Agamemnon, Patroclus, and Hector?

_____
_____
_____
_____
_____
_____
_____

What does this epic say about the hero's role?

_____
_____
_____
_____
_____
_____
_____
_____
_____
_____
_____

Selection Worksheet

Lyric Poems, page 609

READER RESPONSE ACTIVITIES

1. **Reader's Journal, page 610.** Do you ever hope that your name will live on long after your death? What might you do to make future generations remember you? For example, you might decide to effect political change or to create a revolutionary new style of music. On the lines below, write down your thoughts about what you might do to be remembered. Then answer the following questions: How important is it to you to be remembered after your death? Why is it so important, or why isn't it important to you?

   _____

   _____

   _____

   _____

   _____

   _____

   _____

   _____

   _____

   _____

   _____

   _____

   _____

   _____

   _____

2. **Guided Reading.** Answer these questions as you read the selection.

   Page 610: Who does not want love?

   _____

   _____

   Page 610: To what does the speaker compare her feelings for the person addressed?

   _____

   _____

Page 610: What has happened between the speaker and the person whom she addresses?

_____

_____

Page 611: Why wouldn't the speaker take all of these lands in exchange for Cleïs?

_____

_____

Page 611: What does the speaker believe will keep her name from "oblivion"?

_____

_____

Page 611: Why doesn't Sappho wish to be crowned as the best player of the lyre?

_____

_____

Page 612: What does Sappho know? What does she enjoy?

_____

_____

Page 612: What does she refuse to do? What does she say she will do?

_____

_____

Page 612: What does the speaker say has become of Achilles? What does she say about Atreus's sons?

_____

_____

3. **Responding to the Selection, page 613.** Is Sappho a person that you would like to have known? Explain why or why not. Which of her qualities do you find admirable? disagreeable?

_____

_____

_____

_____

_____

_____

_____

_____

_____

_____

_____

_____

_____

_____

_____

_____

_____

_____

_____

RESPONDING IN WRITING

1. **Prewriting: Fragments, page 614.** Freewrite for this activity, jotting down words, phrases, and images that come to mind. Then, review your freewrite. You may find some poetic fragments within it, or you may find some ideas that you would like to adapt into fragments.

_____

_____

_____

_____

_____

_____

_____

_____

_____

_____

_____

_____

_____

_____

_____

2. **Prewriting: Critical Essay, page 615.** Compare and contrast Homeric values with Sapphic values. Use the Venn diagram below to organize your ideas.

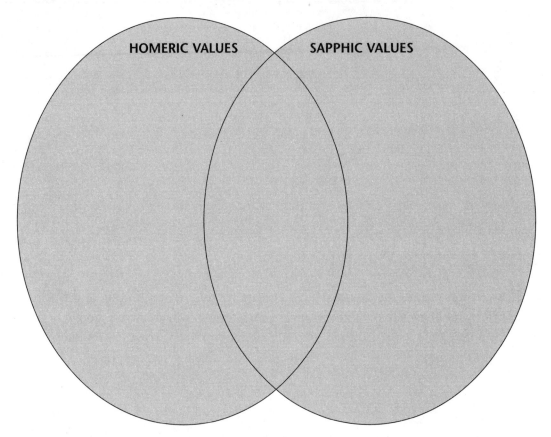

HOMERIC VALUES   SAPPHIC VALUES

Selection Worksheet

Oedipus the King, page 618

READER RESPONSE ACTIVITIES

1. **Reader's Journal, page 620.** Do think it is always best to know the truth? Consider a time when you wanted to know the truth about something and others warned you that it would be best if you did not know. What happened as a result of your push to learn the truth? Write about such an incident on the lines below.

_____

_____

_____

_____

_____

_____

_____

_____

_____

_____

_____

_____

_____

_____

2. **Guided Reading.** Answer these questions as you read the selection.

    Page 621: Why has Oedipus come to hear the suppliants? With what title does he refer to himself? What does he say he will do? What is your first impression of Oedipus?

    _____

    _____

    Page 621: To what does the priest compare the troubles that face Thebes? What is happening in Thebes?

    _____

    _____

Page 622: Why do the people of Thebes turn to Oedipus to help them with their current problem?

_____

_____

Page 622: In what way does Oedipus's sorrow differ from the sorrow the people of Thebes experience?

_____

_____

Page 623: What has Oedipus done to discover the cause of the plague that threatens Thebes?

_____

_____

Page 623: What news does Creon bring back from the oracle? Why is it difficult to carry out the god's demand?

_____

_____

Page 624: What did the only survivor from Laius's party say about the slaying of the king? How do Oedipus's words differ from this man's account?

_____

_____

_____

Page 625: Why is Oedipus intent upon finding the killer?

_____

_____

Page 626: What emotion is expressed in the first strophe? Why might the words of the oracle have aroused such feelings?

_____

_____

_____

Page 626: Summarize the second antistrophe. What does the Chorus ask of Athene?

_____

_____

Page 628: What demand does Oedipus make of the citizens of Thebes?

_____

_____

Page 628: What punishment and curse does Oedipus prescribe for Laius's killer? What does the audience know about the killer that Oedipus does not know?

_____

_____

_____

Page 629: What two things that once belonged to Laius now belong to Oedipus? With what intensity will Oedipus search for the killer of Laius?

_____

_____

_____

Page 629: Why doesn't Oedipus want to ask Apollo's oracle about the killer's identity?

_____

_____

Page 629: Why does the Chorus suggest consulting Teiresias? How does Oedipus respond?

_____

_____

Page 630: What plea does Oedipus make to Teiresias?

_____

_____

Page 630: When is wisdom "terrible"? What does Teiresias regret?

_____

_____

Page 631: Why is Teiresias unwilling to share what he knows with Oedipus? Do you think Oedipus would believe Teiresias if the seer told all that he knew?

_____

_____

_____

Page 632: Of what does Oedipus accuse Teiresias? Why does he make this accusation?

_____

_____

Page 632: What does Teiresias reveal? How does Oedipus react?

_____

_____

Page 633: What does Oedipus say about Teiresias's blindness? Whom does Oedipus really describe?

_____

_____

Page 633: What prediction does Teiresias make?

_____

Page 633: Whom does Oedipus now blame? Explain Teiresias's warning.

_____

_____

Page 634: What excuse does Oedipus use to discount Teiresias's abilities?

_____

_____

Page 634: How does the Chorus feel about the exchange between Oedipus and Teiresias? With what are they concerned?

_____

_____

Page 634: In what way is Oedipus blind? In what way will Oedipus's situation become similar to Teiresias's?

_____

_____

Page 635: What, according to Teiresias, will happen within the day? Why should Oedipus understand the situation? What role does luck play in his destiny?

_____

_____

_____

Page 636: What does Teiresias mean when he says that Oedipus will be shown to be a "true native Theban"? Why does he say that Oedipus will go "tapping his way before him with a stick"?

_____

_____

_____

Page 636: Oedipus's name means "swollen foot." What significance might Oedipus's name and history have upon the Chorus's statement, "Now is the time for him to run with a stronger foot than Pegasus"?

_____

_____

_____

Page 637: What is the Chorus's reaction to Teiresias's words?

_____

_____

Page 637: How do the Thebans, as represented by the Chorus, regard their king?

_____

_____

Page 638: Of what does Oedipus accuse Creon? Does Oedipus have any evidence to prove these accusations?

_____

_____

Page 638: What does Creon accuse Oedipus of lacking? Do you agree with him?

_____

_____

Page 639: Why is Oedipus following this line of questioning?

_____

_____

Page 640: Explain the argument Creon uses to show that he is not trying to take Oedipus's position as king.

_____

_____

_____

Page 640: What does Creon suggest that Oedipus do to prove that he is telling the truth? In what way is the punishment that Creon suggests for himself similar to the punishment Oedipus suggests for the killer of Laius? What about each man's situation makes his claim different?

_____

_____

_____

Page 641: Why does Oedipus insist that he must kill Creon? What objection does Creon make?

_____

_____

Page 642: What does the Chorus advise Oedipus to do? Do you think Oedipus will follow the advice of the Chorus?

_____

_____

Page 642: What reason does the Chorus offer Oedipus for sparing Creon? Why does Oedipus spare him?

_____

_____

Page 642: What does Creon say about Oedipus's nature?

_____

Page 644: How does Jocasta feel about prophecies? What incident does she use to support her claim? How do you think Oedipus feels upon hearing her story?

_____

_____

_____

Page 644: Why does Oedipus question Jocasta about Laius's murder? What do you think is on Oedipus's mind?

_____

_____

Page 645: What does Oedipus fear?

_____

_____

© 1998 EMC Corporation

Page 645: Why do you think the servant asked to be sent away from the city when he returned?

_____

_____

Page 646: What prompted Oedipus to seek the truth about his parentage? What does he learn instead?

_____

_____

Page 646: What does Oedipus do to try to avoid his fate? In what way does his attempt to flee his fate contribute to his fulfilling the prophecy?

_____

_____

_____

Page 647: What does Oedipus realize about his situation? How does he feel upon making this realization?

_____

_____

Page 648: What detail of the shepherd's story does Oedipus want to clarify?

_____

_____

Page 648: For what does the Chorus hope? What may have prompted the Chorus to express this hope?

_____

_____

Page 649: How does the Chorus feel about the gods? about prophecies?

_____

_____

3. **Responding to the Selection, page 650.** What do you think of Oedipus as a leader? Which of his actions or words have most strongly affected your opinion of him? Has that opinion changed over the course of part 1?

Selection Worksheet

Oedipus the King, page 652

READER RESPONSE ACTIVITIES

1. **Reader's Journal, page 652.** Do you believe in fate or destiny, or do you think people have the ability to determine the course of their own lives? On the lines below, write about fate and free will using examples from your own life or from the lives of others to support your opinions.

_____

_____

_____

_____

_____

_____

_____

_____

_____

_____

_____

_____

_____

2. **Guided Reading.** Answer these questions as you read the selection.

   Page 652: Why is Jocasta carrying garlands? What does she request of Apollo?

   _____

   _____

   Page 653: What news does the messenger bring? Why does he think it will be good news to Oedipus? Why does Jocasta also believe it to be good news?

   _____

   _____

   Page 653: How does Oedipus feel about oracles and prophecies?

   _____

   _____

Page 654: Why isn't Oedipus completely comforted by the news of his father's death? What advice does Jocasta give him? Do you think this is sound advice?

_____

_____

Page 655: Why, according to the messenger, are Oedipus's fears empty? What new fears might Oedipus experience in light of this information?

_____

_____

Page 656: Why is Oedipus surprised when the messenger mentions his pained ankles? How does the messenger know of Oedipus's ailment?

_____

_____

Page 656: Why does Jocasta try to dismiss the messenger's story?

_____

_____

Page 657: Why does Jocasta want to put an end to Oedipus's search? Has Oedipus realized what Jocasta knows?

_____

_____

Page 657: Why doesn't Oedipus follow Jocasta's advice? What does this reveal about Oedipus's character? Do you agree that Jocasta's advice is the "best counsel"?

_____

_____

Page 658: How does Jocasta feel about Oedipus's decision to continue his quest for the truth? Why has she run away?

_____

_____

Page 658: What explanation does Oedipus provide for Jocasta's reaction?

_____

_____

Page 658: Whom does Oedipus claim as his mother?

_____

_____

Page 659: What does the Chorus say about the herdsman's character?

_____

_____

Page 659: How does the herdsman feel when questioned about the child he found? Why do you think he feels this way?

_____

_____

Page 660: What does Oedipus threaten to do? What prompts him to make these threats?

_____

_____

Page 660: Why does the herdsman wish that he had died the day he gave the child to the messenger?

_____

_____

Page 661: Why had Jocasta given the child to the herdsman?

_____

_____

Page 661: What was the herdsman supposed to do with the child? What did he do with the boy instead? Why didn't he follow orders?

_____

_____

Page 661: To what event does the Chorus refer?

_____

_____

Page 662: How does the Chorus feel about Oedipus now?

_____

_____

Page 663: Why does the messenger deliver this news rather than allow the Chorus or the audience to see for themselves what has happened?

_____

_____

Page 664: What harm does Oedipus inflict upon himself?

_____

_____

Page 665: How does the Chorus feel as Oedipus is led back into their sight?

_____

_____

Page 665: Whom does Oedipus blame for this bitter situation? Whom does he blame for his present condition?

_____

_____

Page 666: What does Oedipus say about himself? For what does he wish?

_____

_____

Page 666: What does the Chorus think Oedipus should have done rather than blinding himself? Why does it think he should have done this? Do you agree with the Chorus? Why, or why not?

_____

_____

Page 666: Why does Oedipus feel that the punishment he has inflicted upon himself is appropriate?

_____

_____

Page 667: Why, according to Oedipus, shouldn't the Chorus fear to touch him? What has Oedipus recognized about himself?

_____

_____

Page 668: What does Oedipus ask Creon to do? Why does he make this request? Why does Creon hesitate to act upon Oedipus's request?

_____

_____

Page 669: What does Oedipus know about himself? For what does he believe he has been preserved? What attitude does he express toward fate now?

_____

_____

Page 669: About whom does Oedipus worry?

_____

_____

Page 669: What does Oedipus fear will happen to his daughters? What does he ask Creon to do?

_____

_____

Page 671: What does the final speech of the Chorus suggest about life?

_____

_____

3. **Responding to the Selection, page 671.** By the end of the selection do you sympathize with Oedipus, or do you think he is to blame for the trouble and pain he suffers? Explain your response.

_____

_____

_____

_____

_____

_____

_____

_____

_____

_____

_____

_____

_____

RESPONDING IN WRITING

1. **Prewriting: Dialogue, page 673.** Finish each question beginning with the question words below. On your own paper, arrange the questions in a logical order, adding any other questions you would like to ask.

Who _____ ?

What _____ ?

When _____ ?

Where _____ ?

Why _____ ?

How _____ ?

2. **Prewriting: Critical Essay, page 673.** Use the chart below to record the examples and evidence you will use to support your thesis. In the first column note the line number, and in the second column write some key words from the quotation. (Refer to the text for exact quotations when you are drafting your paper.) In the third column, describe how the example is related to the theme of blindness, sight, and truth.

LINE NUMBER	KEY WORDS	RELATIONSHIP TO THEME

Selection Worksheet

"Pericles' Funeral Oration," page 674

READER RESPONSE ACTIVITIES

1. **Reader's Journal, page 675.** What does the word *democracy* mean to you? On the lines below, define *democracy* and write about the benefits you perceive in your own life that come of living in a democracy. What do you think are the responsibilities of the citizens of a democracy? In what way does the democracy of the United States differ from an ideal democracy?

_____

_____

_____

_____

_____

_____

_____

_____

_____

_____

_____

_____

_____

_____

2. **Guided Reading.** Answer these questions as you read the selection.

Page 675: What happens before the funeral procession? What is the significance of the empty coffin? Who takes part in the procession? Where are the dead buried? What does the funeral custom suggest about Athenian attitudes toward their war dead?

_____

_____

Page 676: What problems does Pericles perceive in the tradition of funeral oration? How does Pericles think the dead should be honored?

_____

_____

Page 676: What does Pericles propose to do in his speech?

_____

_____

Page 676: Why is Athenian government called a democracy? What qualities are important in legal decisions and in the choosing of public officials?

_____

_____

Page 677: What connection does Athens have to the rest of the world? What aspect of Athens does Pericles praise in this part of his speech?

_____

_____

Page 677: In what ways does Athens differ from Sparta?

_____

_____

Page 678: What effect does Pericles think Athens has on the rest of Greece? In what way does Athens prove its greatness? How does Pericles think future ages will view Athens?

_____

_____

Page 678: What responsibility does an individual have in a democracy? How should decisions of policy be made?

_____

_____

Page 679: Why has Pericles sung the praises of Athens? In what way does he relate his words to the dead?

_____

_____

Page 679: What does Pericles want his audience to do?

_____

_____

Page 679: What virtues of the dead does Pericles praise? What does Pericles say about the faults of the dead?

_____

_____

Page 680: On what does happiness depend? In what way are people responsible for their own happiness?

_____

_____

Page 680: Why will the future be difficult for the sons and brothers of the dead? What does Pericles say about the reputation of the dead?

_____

_____

Page 680: In what way does Pericles try to comfort the parents of those who have died?

_____

_____

Page 680: What words does Pericles direct to the women in the audience? What does this suggest about his attitude toward women and the role of women in Athenian society?

_____

_____

3. **Responding to the Selection, page 681.** Pericles says, "Make up your minds that happiness depends on being free, and freedom depends on being courageous." Do you agree or disagree with this statement? What kinds of courage do you think members of a democracy need to display during war time? in times of peace?

_____

_____

_____

_____

_____

_____

_____

_____

_____

_____

_____

_____

_____

RESPONDING IN WRITING

1. **Prewriting: Song or Speech of Praise, page 682.** Refer to your response to the
    Reader's Journal activity on page 675 of your textbook. In the space below, outline the
    main points you would like to make about democracy. Use specific examples to
    support the claims you make.

    _____

    _____

    _____

    _____

    _____

    _____

    _____

    _____

2. **Prewriting: Critical Essay, page 682.** Begin by reviewing the selection. As you do
    so, fill in the first column of the chart with the responsibilities or benefits of a
    democracy expressed in Pericles's speech. Then in the second column, note whether
    the same standards apply in the United States. In the third column, give an example to
    support each point that you make about the United States.

ATHENS	UNITED STATES	EXAMPLES

Selection Worksheet

from *From the Founding of the City, Book I*, page 683

READER RESPONSE ACTIVITIES

1. **Reader's Journal, page 684.** Do you think a historian should relate nothing but the facts in a history, or should the historian also describe the legends of the people? Does a historian have a duty to separate fact from fiction for his or her readers? On the lines below, write your opinion of what a historian should and should not do when writing a history.

   _____

   _____

   _____

   _____

   _____

   _____

   _____

   _____

   _____

   _____

   _____

   _____

   _____

   _____

   _____

2. **Guided Reading.** Answer these questions as you read the selection.

   Page 684: Why won't the author affirm or refute legends about Rome's founding?

   _____

   _____

   Page 684: Whom do the Romans claim as their father and the father of their founder? What is the author's attitude toward this claim? According to the author, how should "the nations of the earth" respond to this claim?

   _____

   _____

Page 685: What does King Amulius do to Rhea Silvia and her twin sons?

_____

_____

Page 685: Who discovers the twins and takes care of them?

_____

_____

Page 685: What do the robbers do to the twins?

_____

_____

Page 685: What had Faustulus always suspected? What does Faustulus do?

_____

_____

Page 686: What happens to King Amulius?

_____

_____

Page 686: What does Numitor wonder about Remus?

_____

_____

Page 686: What do Numitor, Romulus, and Remus do to regain Numitor's throne?

_____

_____

Page 687: What did Romulus and Remus want to do in their home region? What prevented them from doing so?

_____

_____

Page 687: What causes the conflict between Romulus and Remus?

_____

_____

3. **Responding to the Selection, page 688.** What makes this history different from other histories you have read? What makes it similar to other histories you have read? Do you agree with the author that "It is the privilege of antiquity to mingle divine things with human, and so to add dignity to the beginnings of cities"?

_____

_____

_____

_____

_____

_____

_____

_____

_____

_____

_____

_____

_____

_____

_____

_____

_____

_____

_____

_____

_____

_____

_____

_____

_____

_____

_____

RESPONDING IN WRITING

1. **Prewriting: Founding Story, page 690.** Work with a group of other students to come up with ideas for your founding story. Choose one of the ideas from the many your group compiles. Fill in the story map below with details about your story.

Story Map

Setting and Mood

Time ——————

——————

Place ——————

Mood ——————

——————

——————

Major characters

——————

——————

Conflict —— internal —— external

——————————————————

Conflict —— internal —— external

——————————————————

Conflict —— internal —— external

——————————————————

Plot
Inciting incident ———————————

——————————————————

Climax ——————————————

——————————————————

Resolution ————————————

——————————————————

Themes ——————————————

2. **Prewriting: Critical Essay, page 690.** As you review the selection, use the following analysis chart to record information for your essay.

KEY PASSAGE	WHAT THIS REVEALS ABOUT THE ROMANS

Selection Worksheet

Selected Poems, page 691

READER RESPONSE ACTIVITIES

1. **Reader's Journal, page 692.** Think about a relationship in your life that changed over time. Write about what this relationship was like in its early stages, its middle stages, and its end stages. What feelings did you have toward the other person at each of these times? How did you express these feelings?

_____

_____

_____

_____

_____

_____

_____

_____

_____

_____

_____

_____

_____

_____

_____

_____

_____

_____

2. **Guided Reading.** Answer these questions as you read the selection.

   Page 692: How long does the speaker expect his love to last?

   _____

   _____

   Page 692: What does the speaker say about a woman's words? What does he mean?

   _____

   _____

Page 693: How does the speaker feel? What do you imagine the cause of these feelings to be?

_____

_____

Page 693: Whom does the speaker blame for his misery? How does the speaker feel about this person?

_____

_____

3. **Responding to the Selection, page 693.** Imagine that you are Lesbia, whom these poems address. How would you feel when you read each poem? Imagine how you might respond to Catullus. Write a response to each poem in the form of a letter or a poem, or role play with a partner a series of discussions between Catullus and Lesbia at each stage of their relationship.

_____

_____

_____

_____

_____

_____

_____

_____

_____

_____

_____

_____

_____

_____

_____

_____

_____

_____

_____

RESPONDING IN WRITING

1. **Prewriting: Lyric Poem, page 695.** Choose a subject about which you have strong feelings. On the lines below, freewrite to express your feelings about the subject and to craft images that show how you feel.

_____

_____

_____

_____

_____

_____

_____

_____

_____

_____

_____

_____

_____

_____

_____

_____

_____

_____

_____

_____

_____

2. **Prewriting: Critical Essay, page 695.** To gather ideas for your essay, fill in the chart below with information about the song lyrics and about the poem by Catullus.

	POEM	SONG LYRICS
Speaker		
Speaker's attitude toward beloved		
Change in feelings over the course of the work		
Change in feelings over the course of the relationship		

Selection Worksheet

from *The Lives of the Noble Grecians and Romans*, page 696

READER RESPONSE ACTIVITIES

1. **Reader's Journal, page 697.** Have you ever offered flattery to get something you wanted? Have you ever been flattered? Of what benefit is flattery? What problems might flattery cause?

_____

_____

_____

_____

_____

_____

_____

_____

_____

_____

_____

_____

2. **Guided Reading.** Answer these questions as you read the selection.

Page 697: Why isn't Brutus eager to overthrow Cæsar? What relationship exists between the two?

_____

_____

Page 698: What warning does the soothsayer give Cæsar? What is Cæsar's attitude toward this warning? What is the soothsayer's response to Cæsar's "raillery"?

_____

_____

Page 698: Why do those who want to prevent Cæsar from becoming king want Brutus to join their cause? What do they do to achieve this goal?

_____

_____

Page 698: What strange omens indicate that something "unavoidable" is about to happen?

_____

_____

Page 699: Who tries to warn Cæsar of the plot against him? Why is the warning ineffectual?

_____

_____

Page 699: How does Decimus Brutus lure Cæsar to the senate?

_____

_____

Page 699: What does the narrator see as evidence of some "supernatural influence" over Cæsar's fate?

_____

_____

Page 700: What is Cæsar's reaction when he discovers that Brutus has turned against him?

_____

_____

Page 700: Who is loyal to Cæsar? What do the conspirators do to keep this person from interfering?

_____

_____

Page 700: Where does Cæsar fall? What does the narrator say about this scene?

_____

_____

Page 700: What happens after Cæsar is killed?

_____

_____

Page 701: How do people react to Cæsar's murder after hearing Brutus's speech?

_____

_____

Page 701: What changes the way the people of Rome feel about the murder? What attitude does the populace adopt toward the conspirators?

_____

_____

Page 702: What events in the natural world does the narrator say were the result of Cæsar's murder?

_____

_____

Page 702: What shows that Brutus's part in the murder was not pleasing to the gods?

_____

_____

Page 702: What had Cæsar pursued throughout his life? What were the results of the pursuit?

_____

_____

Page 703: Why does Antony command Cleopatra to appear before him?

_____

_____

Page 703: What effect does the narrator say Antony's love for Cleopatra had upon him?

_____

_____

Page 704: Why is Cleopatra so sure of herself?

_____

_____

Page 704: What makes Cleopatra so attractive?

_____

_____

Page 704: What does Cleopatra do "in mockery" of Antony's urgent summons?

_____

_____

Page 704: What evidence is there of Cleopatra's linguistic ability?

_____

_____

Page 704: What message is sent to the multitude?

_____

_____

Page 705: What does Antony do to impress Cleopatra?

_____

_____

Page 705: What does Cleopatra do when she discovers Antony's trick? What does she tell him to do?

_____

_____

3. **Responding to the Selection, page 706.** Explain why you did or did not sympathize with Julius Cæsar. Can you justify Brutus's motivations for his actions? Why, or why not? Whom do you find more interesting, Antony or Cleopatra? Why?

_____

_____

_____

_____

_____

_____

_____

_____

_____

_____

_____

_____

_____

_____

_____

_____

_____

_____

_____

_____

_____

_____

_____

_____

RESPONDING IN WRITING

1. **Prewriting: Description, page 707.** After you have decided upon a character, begin gathering details for your description. Use the sensory detail chart below to record vivid images.

2.

CHARACTER DESCRIPTION				
SIGHT	SOUND	TOUCH	TASTE	SMELL

Prewriting: Critical Essay, page 707. To compare and contrast history with biography, you must be clear on the purpose and form of each. To explore these differences and similarities, jot down some notes in response to each of the following questions:

What is a history?

_____

What is a biography?

_____

In what ways do biographies differ from histories?

_____

_____

_____

_____

_____

In what way is the aim or goal of a biographer similar to that of a historian?

_____

_____

_____

_____

_____

What can a biography reveal about the history of a people, country, or institution?

_____

_____

_____

_____

_____

_____

Selection Worksheet

9.1

from *The Story of the Grail*, page 722

READER RESPONSE ACTIVITIES

1. **Reader's Journal, page 723**. Have you ever seen something strange, interesting, or wondrous that you did not understand? Did you ask questions to try to gain an understanding? Did you learn about it in another way? Describe this thing or event, and explain what you know about its significance.

   _____

   _____

   _____

   _____

   _____

   _____

   _____

   _____

   _____

   _____

   _____

2. **Guided Reading.** Answer these questions as you read the selection.

   Page 723: What does Perceval want to know from the fishermen and what do they tell him?

   _____

   _____

   Page 723: What does Perceval first see after following the fisherman's directions?

   _____

   _____

   Page 724: What appears to Perceval? In what way does Perceval's opinion of the fisherman change?

   _____

   _____

Page 725: What greeting does the lord of the castle offer Perceval? What is the lord unable to do?

_____

_____

Page 725: What is impressive about the sword the squire brings into the room? What does the squire say the lord may do with this sword?

_____

_____

Page 725: What does Perceval notice about the lance that is carried through the room? Why doesn't he ask about this strange occurrence?

_____

_____

Page 726: What does the maiden carry through the room?

_____

Page 726: What would Perceval like to ask about the Grail? Why does he refrain from asking? What comment does the narrator make about Perceval's silence?

_____

_____

_____

Page 726: What happens while Perceval and the lord are eating? Why does Perceval keep silent? What does he resolve to do?

_____

_____

Page 727: What does Perceval set out to find? What happens when Perceval is leaving the castle?

_____

_____

Page 727: What is surprising about the household to which Perceval awakes in the morning?

_____

_____

Page 728: What does the maiden explain to Perceval about the Fisher King?

_____

_____

Page 728: Why is the lady surprised by the appearance of Perceval?

_____

_____

Page 729: Why is Perceval's failure to question the wondrous things he observed such a wretched thing? What does Perceval learn about his mother?

_____

_____

Page 729: About what does the youth have to guess? Why is this lack of knowledge unusual?

_____

_____

3. **Responding to the Selection, page 730.** Upon hearing what the maiden has to say, how would you feel if you were Perceval? What do you think Perceval will do in response to this news?

_____

_____

_____

_____

_____

_____

_____

_____

_____

_____

_____

_____

_____

_____

_____

RESPONDING IN WRITING

1. **Prewriting: Advice Column, page 731.** Before drafting your column, take some time to freewrite about advice you have been given, how you reacted to the advice, and the effect that the advice had on you.

   _____

   _____

   _____

   _____

   _____

   _____

   _____

   _____

2. **Prewriting: Critical Essay, page 731.** Review the selection keeping the following questions in mind: How does Perceval face difficulties? How does he interact with others? What guides his actions? As you review the text take notes on material that answers these questions or that in some way illuminates Perceval as a character.

   _____

   _____

   _____

   _____

   _____

   _____

   _____

   _____

   _____

   _____

   _____

   _____

   _____

   _____

Selection Worksheet

from *Tristan*, page 732

READER RESPONSE ACTIVITIES

1. **Reader's Journal, page 733.** Write on the lines below about a time when you felt an emotion so strong that you could not control or hide it. What was this emotion, and why did you think you had to control or hide it? What happened when you finally revealed your feelings?

_____

_____

_____

_____

_____

_____

_____

_____

_____

_____

_____

_____

_____

2. **Guided Reading.** Answer these questions as you read the selection.

   Page 734: What is the elder Isolde doing?

   _____

   _____

   Page 734: What does the elder Isolde tell Brangane to do? About what does she warn her?

   _____

   _____

   Page 734: How does Isolde feel about Tristan?

   _____

   _____

Page 735: Why is Isolde upset?

_____

_____

Page 735: How does Tristan treat Isolde?

_____

_____

Page 735: Why do many people weep at Isolde's departure?

_____

_____

Page 735: Why does Isolde hate Tristan?

_____

_____

Page 735: According to Tristan, why should Isolde be eager to marry Mark?

_____

_____

Page 736: What circumstances does Isolde say she would prefer?

_____

_____

Page 737: What does Brangane realize about what has just occurred? How does she feel about this occurrence?

_____

_____

Page 737: Why does the captain bring the boat to shore?

_____

_____

Page 737: What effect does the potion have on Tristan and Isolde?

_____

_____

Page 737: What does the lady-in-waiting give to Tristan and Isolde?

_____

_____

Page 738: What feelings make Tristan try to hide his love for Isolde?

_____

_____

Page 738: What are the only things Isolde can think about?

_____

_____

Page 738: What feelings make Isolde try to hide her love for Tristan?

_____

_____

Page 739: What effect does the author say love will always have on people?

_____

_____

3. **Responding to the Selection, page 739.** "Love seems fairer than before and so Love's rule endures. Were Love to seem the same as before, Love's rule would soon wither away." Explain in your own words the meaning of this moral. Do you agree or disagree with this sentiment?

_____

_____

_____

_____

_____

_____

_____

_____

_____

_____

_____

_____

_____

_____

_____

RESPONDING IN WRITING

1. **Prewriting: Continuation, page 741.** Do a focused freewrite in response to the following questions: Will anyone discover that Tristan and Isolde drank the love potion? Will the elder Isolde who concocted the love potion be able to intercede? Will Tristan and Isolde give up their love for each other? If not, will Mark discover their love?

_____

_____

_____

_____

_____

_____

_____

_____

_____

_____

_____

_____

2. **Prewriting: Critical Essay, page 741.** In the space below, make a rough outline of your essay. For more information on rough outlines, see the Language Arts Survey 1.12, "Outlining."

_____

_____

_____

_____

_____

_____

_____

_____

_____

_____

_____

_____

Selection Worksheet

9.3

"Lady Maria, your worth and excellence," page 742

READER RESPONSE ACTIVITIES

1. **Reader's Journal, page 743.** Think of a time when you had to request something important from someone. Describe your request. What did you do to try to convince the person to grant your request? Did you compliment the person? offer a rationale? beg? Was your request granted? Write about what you did to make the person take your request seriously.

   _____

   _____

   _____

   _____

   _____

2. **Guided Reading.** Answer these questions as you read the selection.

   Page 743: What draws the speaker to Lady Maria?

   _____

   _____

   Page 743: What does the speaker ask of Lady Maria?

   _____

   _____

   Page 744: Why would loving the speaker benefit Lady Maria?

   _____

   _____

3. **Responding to the Selection, page 745.** How would you feel if such a poem were addressed to you? What response would you give the speaker?

   _____

   _____

   _____

   _____

RESPONDING IN WRITING

1. **Prewriting: Lyric Poem, page 746.** After choosing a request, freewrite for a few minutes about ways in which you might make the request.

_____

_____

_____

_____

_____

_____

_____

_____

_____

_____

_____

_____

2. **Prewriting: Critical Essay, page 746.** In the first column of the following chart, list similarities between the movement of devotion to Mary and the development of courtly love. In the second column, identify examples from the poem that illustrate aspects of the movements listed in the left column.

SIMILARITIES	EXAMPLES FROM POEM

Selection Worksheet

from *The Divine Comedy*, page 747

READER RESPONSE ACTIVITIES

1. **Reader's Journal, page 748.** What people, places, and things do you associate with the words *good* and *virtuous*? What people, places, and things come to mind when you think about the words *evil* and *immoral*? What representations of good and evil have you seen in books, movies, and television? List at least three representations of good and three representations of evil. Then pick the best one from each category to discuss in class.

_____

_____

_____

_____

_____

_____

_____

_____

_____

_____

_____

2. **Guided Reading.** Answer these questions as you read the selection.

Page 749: Where does Dante find himself? What is the place like? How does it make him feel?

_____

_____

Page 749: From where did Dante wander to this place?

_____

_____

Page 749: With what did the shoulders of the little hill glow? How does this sight make Dante feel? What does he turn to do?

_____

_____

Page 749: What creature blocks Dante's way?

_____

_____

Page 750: What other beasts does Dante encounter? What is terrifying about these creatures?

_____

_____

Page 750: Where do the beasts drive Dante?

_____

_____

Page 750: Who appears before Dante? Why is Dante familiar with this figure?

_____

_____

Page 751: Why can't Dante travel past the beasts? Which way must he go?

_____

_____

Page 751: Why is Virgil unable to accompany Dante for his entire journey?

_____

_____

Page 752: Where does Dante say he is willing to be led?

_____

Page 753: What does Beatrice demand that Dante do?

_____

_____

Page 754: What things did Dante mistakenly treasure?

_____

_____

Page 754: Why is it important for Dante to speak of and understand his sins? How does Dante feel after he confesses his sins?

_____

_____

Page 754: What has Dante gained from his love of mortal things? What does Beatrice say he should have learned?

_____

_____

Page 755: Whom does Dante find when he returns to consciousness? What does she make him do, and why?

_____

_____

Page 756: What are the Four Maidens, appearing as nymphs, supposed to be doing for Dante?

_____

_____

Page 756: Where must Dante look first? What does he see?

_____

_____

Page 756: What effect does Beatrice's smile have on Dante?

_____

_____

3. **Responding to the Selection, page 757.** In what way is your image of the afterlife similar to or different from Dante's? Explain.

_____

_____

_____

_____

_____

_____

_____

_____

_____

_____

_____

_____

RESPONDING IN WRITING

1. **Prewriting: Journey Tale, page 758.** In the space below make a map of the journey your character will take. On your own paper, write a paragraph describing the setting, the main obstacles, and the goal.

2. **Prewriting: Critical Essay, page 758.** Identify your thesis. Then in the space below, begin an outline of your essay. Add headings and subheadings as necessary and use your own paper to complete the outline.

I. Dante as humankind

A. _____

    1. _____

    2. _____

B. _____

    1. _____

    2. _____

_____

_____

_____

Selection Worksheet

"Ballade," page 759

READER RESPONSE ACTIVITIES

1. **Reader's Journal, page 760.** Imagine that you have been sentenced to death. What would you think about? Would you worry about the pain of your execution? about what others would think of you? about your condition in the afterlife? Would you accept the sentence with resignation, or would you be angry and struggle against it? On the lines below, write about what you would want to express to others if you received such a sentence.

_____

_____

_____

_____

_____

_____

_____

_____

_____

_____

_____

_____

_____

_____

_____

_____

2. **Guided Reading.** Answer these questions as you read the selection.

   Page 760: According to the speakers, why should living human beings pity the speakers? What do the speakers call the living human beings?

   _____

   _____

   Page 760: What is the condition of the speakers? How can you tell the speakers are dead? What do the speakers ask of the living?

   _____

   _____

Page 760: What keeps the speakers from "hellfire"?

_____

_____

Page 761: What do the speakers warn others not to do? Why shouldn't others do this?

_____

_____

Page 761: According to the speakers, why shouldn't they "fall into hell's dominion"?

_____

_____

3. **Responding to the Selection, page 762.** How would you feel if you encountered the speakers as they are described in this poem? What would your attitude toward them be? Imagine that you then hear the speakers' plea. Would this plea change your attitude toward the speakers? If so, in what way? If not, why not?

_____

_____

_____

_____

_____

_____

_____

_____

_____

_____

_____

_____

_____

_____

_____

_____

_____

_____

_____

_____

RESPONDING IN WRITING

1. **Prewriting: Epitaph, page 763.** Before writing your epitaph, freewrite about how you would like people to remember you when you die and what message you would like to share with the living.

——
——
——
——
——
——
——
——
——
——
——
——
——
——
——
——
——
——
——
——
——
——
——
——
——
——
——
——
——
——

2. **Prewriting: Critical Essay, page 764.** Use the following Venn diagram to compare and contrast the ideas expressed in "Ballade" to medieval attitudes toward death.

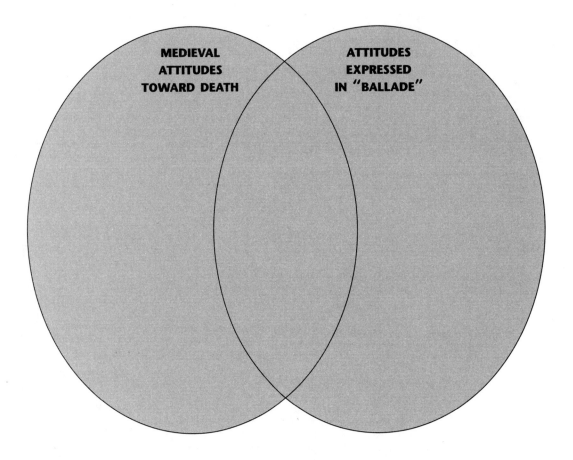

MEDIEVAL ATTITUDES TOWARD DEATH

ATTITUDES EXPRESSED IN "BALLADE"

Name _____ Class _____ Date _____

Selection Worksheet

from *The Tale of Genji*, page 765

9.6

READER RESPONSE ACTIVITIES

1. **Reader's Journal, page 766**. What images come to mind when you think about royal courts, emperors, and princes? What people, places, and events do you expect to find in a romantic adventure novel about a royal court and a popular prince?

_____

_____

_____

_____

_____

_____

_____

_____

_____

_____

_____

_____

_____

_____

_____

_____

_____

_____

2. **Guided Reading.** Answer these questions as you read the selection.

Page 766: Why were the "grand ladies" resentful of the woman, Genji's mother? What feelings did the emperor have for this woman?

_____

_____

Page 767: In what way was the woman's new child a "private treasure"?

_____

_____

3. **Responding to the Selection, page 768.** What are your feelings about the world in which Genji's mother lives, as described in the opening of *The Tale of Genji*? Would you want to live in such a world? Why, or why not?

_____

_____

_____

_____

_____

_____

_____

RESPONDING IN WRITING

1. **Prewriting: Introduction, page 769.** In the space below, freewrite about possible settings and central actions for your fantasy or science fiction novel or computer game.

_____

_____

_____

_____

_____

_____

_____

_____

2. **Prewriting: Critical Essay, page 769.** In the space below, write a rough outline for your essay. Use the judgments you are making as heads. Below each judgment note supporting details from the selection. Continue your rough outline on your own paper if necessary.

_____

_____

_____

_____

_____

_____

_____

Selection Worksheet

9.7

from *The Pillow Book*, page 770

READER RESPONSE ACTIVITIES

1. **Reader's Journal, page 771.** Take a few moments to record on the lines below your thoughts about something that happened to you today or about particular people you have dealt with recently. Then think about how writing helps to clarify your thoughts and feelings. In what ways do you find writing in a journal to be a useful or interesting activity?

_____

_____

_____

_____

_____

_____

_____

_____

_____

_____

_____

_____

_____

_____

2. **Guided Reading.** Answer these questions as you read the selection.

   Page 771: What time of day does Sei Shōnagon enjoy most during each season of the year?

   _____

   _____

   Page 771: What type of woman fills Sei Shōnagon with scorn? What does she feel these women should do differently?

   _____

   _____

   Page 772: In what ways are women at court different from other women?

   _____

   _____

Page 773: What are Sei Shōnagon's feelings about rowdy men in public? What is distasteful about the behavior of these men?

_____

_____

Page 773: In what sort of world does Sei Shōnagon live, judging from her use of phrases such as "someone of no importance" and "the sort of visitor whose presence commands one's best behavior"?

_____

_____

Page 773: How does Sei Shōnagon feel about elderly people?

_____

_____

Page 774: Why might someone like Sei Shōnagon enjoy piecing together someone's torn letter?

_____

_____

Page 774: What does Sei Shōnagon say pleases her more than having something nice happen to herself? Is this statement surprising? Why, or why not?

_____

_____

3. **Responding to the Selection, page 775.** What are your reactions to Sei Shōnagon's personality, beliefs, and the world in which she lived? Is she somebody you would like to have known? Why, or why not?

_____

_____

_____

_____

_____

_____

_____

_____

_____

_____

RESPONDING IN WRITING

1. Prewriting: Pillow Book, page 777. Before you begin writing, brainstorm a list of topics that you would like to write about.

_____

_____

_____

_____

_____

_____

_____

_____

_____

_____

_____

_____

_____

_____

_____

_____

_____

_____

_____

_____

_____

_____

_____

_____

_____

_____

_____

_____

2. **Prewriting: Critical Essay, page 777**. First identify several words that describe Sei Shōnagon's character. Write these on the heading lines below. Under each head, note examples from *The Pillow Book* that support your opinion.

_____

_____

_____

_____

_____

_____

_____

_____

_____

_____

_____

_____

_____

_____

_____

_____

_____

_____

_____

Selection Worksheet

from the Koran, page 778

READER RESPONSE ACTIVITIES

1. **Reader's Journal, page 779.** What are some of your beliefs about your role in the universe? What people, books, events, or religious experiences have guided and shaped your beliefs about yourself and this perceived role?

_____

_____

_____

_____

_____

_____

_____

_____

_____

_____

_____

_____

2. **Guided Reading.** Answer these questions as you read the selection.

   Page 779: What words are used to describe God? Of what is God sovereign?

   _____

   _____

   Page 779: Onto what path do people wish to be guided? What path do they wish to avoid?

   _____

   _____

   Page 779: When will each soul "know what it has done and what it has failed to do"?

   _____

   _____

Page 780: Which people will "dwell in bliss" on Judgment Day? Who will suffer on Judgment Day?

_____

_____

Page 780: What is the Day of Judgment?

_____

_____

Page 780: To what should Mohammed look forward? Why?

_____

_____

Page 780: What has the Lord done for Mohammed? What should he proclaim?

_____

_____

3. **Responding to the Selection, page 782.** What thoughts and feelings do you associate with the phrase *Judgment Day*? Imagine that you were experiencing Judgment Day as described in this selection. What do you think the results of the judgment would be? Why?

_____

_____

_____

_____

_____

_____

_____

_____

_____

_____

_____

_____

_____

_____

RESPONDING IN WRITING

1. **Prewriting: Guide, page 783.** Review your response to the Reader's Journal activity for this selection. Then take ten minutes to freewrite about beliefs and experiences that have most influenced your life.

_____

_____

_____

_____

_____

_____

_____

_____

_____

_____

_____

_____

_____

_____

_____

_____

_____

_____

_____

_____

_____

_____

_____

_____

_____

2. **Prewriting: Critical Essay, page 783.** Use the Venn diagram below to record differences and similarities between the moral messages presented in the passages from the Koran and in the excerpt from *The Divine Comedy*. Use your own paper if you need additional room.

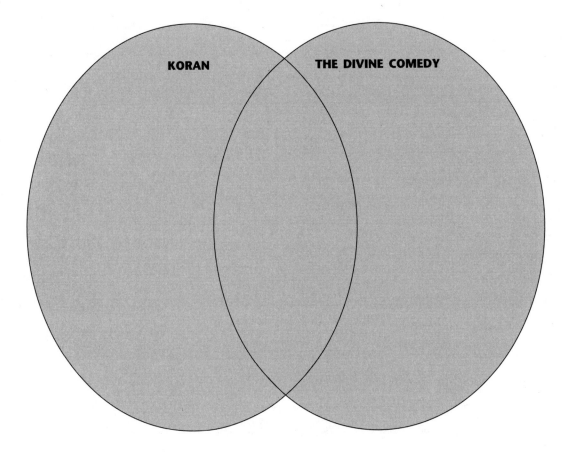

KORAN

THE DIVINE COMEDY

Selection Worksheet

"The Fisherman and the Jinnee," page 784

READER RESPONSE ACTIVITIES

1. **Reader's Journal, page 785.** Consider the phrases "Do unto others as you would have them do unto you" and "Life for life,/ Eye for eye, tooth for tooth, hand for hand, foot for foot,/ Burning for burning, wound for wound, stripe for stripe." With which of these ideas do you agree? Which of these mottoes best reflects the way you live? Explain why you prefer one motto to the other.

_____

_____

_____

_____

_____

_____

_____

_____

_____

2. **Guided Reading.** Answer these questions as you read the selection

Page 785: Why is the fisherman concerned as he casts his net for the fourth time?

_____

_____

Page 785: What did the fisherman catch the first three times he cast his net?

_____

_____

Page 786: What is the fisherman's reaction when he sees the jinnee?

_____

_____

Page 786: In what way did the jinnee change the way he planned to treat his rescuer over the years?

_____

_____

Page 786: Why are the fisherman's feelings about the jinnee justified?

_____

_____

Page 787: How does the fisherman's cunning save him from the jinnee?

_____

_____

Page 787: What fate does the fisherman say that the jinnee deserves?

_____

_____

Page 788: What does the doctor say that he will do for the king? What will he not do?

_____

_____

Page 788: How does the doctor prepare to cure the king?

_____

_____

Page 789: How does the vizier respond to the king's treatment of the doctor?

_____

_____

Page 789: What does the vizier say about the doctor?

_____

_____

Page 789: What is the king's reaction to the vizier's warning?

_____

_____

Page 790: Why does the king become angry?

_____

_____

Page 790: What punishment does the king inflict upon the falcon? What does the king realize about the falcon's actions?

_____

_____

Page 791: What plea does the doctor make to the king?

_____

_____

Page 791: What effect does the story about the falcon and the king have on the vizier?

_____

_____

Page 792: What happened as the king tried to follow the doctor's instructions about the book?

_____

_____

Page 792: In what way is the story of the king and the physician similar to the story of the fisherman and the jinnee?

_____

_____

3. **Responding to the Selection, page 793.** Do you agree with the way the fisherman treated the jinnee? What would you have done in his situation? Do you think the jinnee deserved his fate? Explain.

_____

_____

_____

_____

_____

_____

_____

_____

_____

_____

_____

RESPONDING IN WRITING

1. **Prewriting: Frame Tale, page 794.** In the space below, summarize the frame that connects the stories in your tale and note the theme of the tales. Then outline the story that you will write.

   Summary of Frame

   _____

   _____

   _____

   Themes

   _____

   _____

   _____

   Outline of Story

   _____

   _____

   _____

2. **Prewriting: Critical Essay, page 794.** Fill in the following chart with details about the themes of the stories.

	FISHERMAN	KING YUNAN	KING SINDBAD AND THE FALCON
THEME			
RELATIONSHIP TO OTHER THEMES			

Selection Worksheet

9.10

from *The Rubáiyát of Omar Khayyám*, page 796

READER RESPONSE ACTIVITIES

1. **Reader's Journal, page 797.** Have you ever let an opportunity slip by and regretted it later? Have you ever planned for an important moment only to be disappointed by how it turned out? Write about one such experience and what, if anything, you learned from it.

_____

_____

_____

_____

_____

_____

_____

_____

_____

_____

_____

2. **Guided Reading.** Answer these questions as you read the selection.

   Page 797: What four things would turn a wilderness into a paradise for the speaker of this poem?

   _____

   _____

   Page 797: Does the speaker think we should live for today or for tomorrow?

   _____

   _____

   Page 797: What do lines 13–15 suggest about life?

   _____

   _____

Page 798: What is the common fate of all? What happens to people's hopes?

_____

_____

Page 798: Why cannot the great hunter be awakened? Of what significance are his feats now?

_____

_____

Page 799: What does the speaker want his beloved to do?

_____

_____

Page 799: What does the speaker think we should do, given that we shall all die?

_____

_____

3. **Responding to the Selection, page 800.** What lines from this selection stand out for you? Why?

_____

_____

_____

_____

_____

_____

_____

_____

_____

_____

_____

_____

_____

_____

RESPONDING IN WRITING

1. **Prewriting: Recipe for Paradise, page 801.** Begin by freewriting about things that are important to you and things that make you happy. Think about people, places, objects, and activities.

_____

_____

_____

_____

_____

_____

_____

_____

_____

_____

_____

_____

_____

_____

_____

_____

_____

_____

_____

_____

_____

_____

_____

_____

_____

2. Prewriting: Critical Essay, page 801. First write your thesis. Then for each stanza that supports your thesis, write a brief explanation of how it contributes to the theme. Begin in the space below and use your own paper to take notes on the rest of the stanzas.

Thesis _____
_____
_____
_____
_____
_____

Stanza 12 _____
_____
_____
_____
_____
_____
_____

Stanza 13 _____
_____
_____
_____
_____
_____
_____

Stanza 14 _____
_____
_____
_____
_____
_____
_____

Selection Worksheet

from the *Mathnavi*, page 804

READER RESPONSE ACTIVITIES

1. **Reader's Journal, page 805.** Do you believe there are aspects of the universe that people cannot understand? What do you think are the limits to human knowledge? Why do you think some people try to reach far beyond those limits?

_____

_____

_____

_____

_____

_____

_____

_____

_____

_____

_____

_____

2. **Guided Reading.** Answer these questions as you read the selection.

   Page 805: Who ran into Solomon's hall of justice? Why was he upset?

   _____

   _____

   Page 805: What does the nobleman ask of the king? Why does he ask this? Does the king grant him the favor?

   _____

   _____

   Page 805: Why did Azrael look at the man in astonishment rather than with anger?

   _____

   _____

Page 806: Where was the elephant? What different things did the people think the elephant was?

_____

_____

Page 806: Had people walked into the elephant exhibition with candles, in what way would their descriptions of the elephant have changed?

_____

_____

3. **Responding to the Selection, page 807.** Throughout history, people have used stories to teach lessons. Why do you think this is so? What stories that taught lessons have you been told? Did these stories help you to learn and remember the lessons? Explain why or why not.

_____

_____

_____

_____

_____

_____

_____

_____

_____

_____

_____

_____

_____

_____

_____

_____

RESPONDING IN WRITING

1. **Prewriting: Parable, page 808.** First identify the lesson that you would like to teach through a parable. Then freewrite to find a way to convey this message.

Lesson: _____

_____

_____

_____

Ways message might be conveyed or illustrated: _____

_____

_____

_____

_____

_____

_____

_____

_____

_____

_____

_____

_____

_____

_____

_____

_____

_____

_____

_____

_____

2. **Prewriting: Critical Essay, page 808.** In the space below, identify what the symbols might represent. Then briefly note the way in which such a symbol might be related to the theme.

The nobleman represents:

_____

Way in which the symbol is related to the theme:

_____

_____

Azrael represents:

_____

Way in which the symbol is related to the theme:

_____

_____

The darkness represents:

_____

Way in which the symbol is related to the theme:

_____

_____

The elephant represents:

_____

Way in which the symbol is related to the theme:

_____

_____

Selection Worksheet

"Federigo's Falcon," page 822

READER RESPONSE ACTIVITIES

1. **Reader's Journal, page 823.** What is the most generous thing you have ever done for another person? What prompted you to behave in a generous manner? Write about this experience on the lines below.

_____

_____

_____

_____

_____

_____

_____

_____

_____

_____

2. **Guided Reading.** Answer these questions as you read the selection.

Page 823: What does Federigo do to win Monna Giovanna's love?

_____

_____

Page 823: Who will inherit the husband's money should his son die?

_____

_____

Page 824: Why doesn't the boy ask for the falcon? What does the boy ask for once he becomes ill?

_____

_____

Page 824: What is Federigo's only means of support?

_____

_____

Page 825: For what is Federigo searching?

_____

_____

Page 825: What does Federigo do? How does he feel about doing this?

_____

_____

Page 825: What compensation does Monna Giovanna offer Federigo?

_____

_____

Page 825: In what way does Federigo's response demonstrate the ideals of courtly love?

_____

_____

Page 825: What does Monna Giovanna say was the cause of her ignoring Federigo?

_____

_____

Page 826: What reason does Monna Giovanna give for requesting the falcon? According to Monna, why should Federigo give her the falcon?

_____

_____

Page 826: Why does Federigo weep?

_____

_____

Page 826: How does Monna Giovanna feel about what Federigo has done?

_____

_____

Page 826: What happens to the son? What reasons for this occurrence does the narrator suggest?

_____

_____

Page 827: Who is the only person Monna Giovanna would consider marrying?

_____

_____

Page 827: In what way has Federigo changed?

_____

_____

3. **Responding to the Selection, page 828.** If you were in Federigo's position, would you have acted as he does, or would you have acted differently? Explain. If you were in Monna Giovanna's position, would you have acted as she does? Why, or why not? What might you have done differently?

_____

_____

_____

_____

_____

_____

_____

_____

_____

RESPONDING IN WRITING

1. **Prewriting: Continuation, page 829.** Do a focused freewrite in response to the following questions: What would Federigo and Monna be like as a married couple? Would their relationship be a happy one? Would Federigo feel content in the relationship, or would he still feel as if he must constantly prove himself to Monna? Would Monna love Federigo, or would she resent the fact that her brothers urged her to marry?

_____

_____

_____

_____

_____

_____

_____

2. **Prewriting: Critical Essay, page 829.** Use the chart below to gather examples of realistic and unrealistic elements from the story.

REALISTIC	UNREALISTIC

Selection Worksheet

10.2

from *Orlando Furioso,* page 830

READER RESPONSE ACTIVITIES

1. **Reader's Journal, page 831.** On the lines below, express your thoughts about gender roles. Before writing, consider the following questions: What do you think a man should be like? What do you think a woman should be like? Is there anything that you believe men or women cannot or should not do because of their gender?

    _____

    _____

    _____

    _____

    _____

    _____

    _____

    _____

    _____

    _____

2. **Guided Reading.** Answer these questions as you read the selection.

    Page 831: What words are used to describe the knight?

    _____

    _____

    Page 831: What has the arrival of the knight done to Sacripante's plans?

    _____

    _____

    Page 832: Which of the knights is bigger and stronger?

    _____

    _____

    Page 832: What is the result of the conflict?

    _____

    _____

Page 834: What does Angelica do for Sacripante? How does Sacripante feel about what has happened to him?

_____

_____

Page 834: In what way does Angelica comfort Sacripante? Do you think that she is sincere in her consolation? Why, or why not?

_____

_____

Page 835: What does the envoy reveal?

_____

_____

Page 835: How does Sacripante feel about what the envoy has told him?

_____

_____

Page 836: What type of a knight is Pinabello?

_____

_____

Page 837: What warning does Pinabello give Bradamante? What do you think will happen? Why?

_____

_____

Page 838: Why has King Charles given Bradamante governorship of Marseilles?

_____

_____

Page 838: Why is Bradamante "suspended between yes and no"? What does she decide to do?

_____

_____

Page 839: What does Pinabello decide to do? Why?

_____

_____

Page 840: For what is Pinabello looking? What does he find?

_____

_____

Page 840: What new plan has Pinabello decided upon?

_____

_____

Page 840: What does Pinabello say he has seen in the hollow? Has he really seen this?

_____

_____

Page 841: What does Pinabello do?

_____

Page 841: What saves Bradamante from death?

_____

_____

Page 842: Why might taking away a knight's horse be such a terrible deed?

_____

_____

Page 842: What surprising thing does Bradamante find in the cave?

_____

_____

Page 843: What does Bradamante do in this holy place?

_____

_____

Page 843: Who greets Bradamante? In what way did Pinabello speak more truly than he knew?

_____

_____

Page 843: Who predicted Bradamante's arrival?

_____

_____

Page 843: What has happened to Merlin? What can Merlin do?

_____

_____

Page 844: What does Merlin say about Bradamante? What two of her qualities does he value?

_____

_____

Page 844: What does Merlin say Bradamante's offspring will do?

_____

_____

Page 844: What will happen to Ruggiero? How do you know?

_____

_____

3. **Responding to the Selection, page 845.** Explain whether you find Bradamante to be heroic. Are other characters in the selection heroic? Why, or why not?

_____

_____

_____

_____

_____

_____

_____

_____

_____

_____

_____

_____

_____

_____

_____

RESPONDING IN WRITING

1. **Prewriting:** *Ottava Rima*, **page 846**. In the space below, outline your group's plot. Then identify the part that you will write and create a story map for your part of the plot.

_____

_____

_____

_____

_____

_____

_____

_____

_____

_____

_____

_____

_____

_____

Story Map

Setting and Mood

Time _____

_____

Place _____

Mood _____

_____

Major characters

_____

_____

Conflict ___ internal ___ external

_____

Conflict ___ internal ___ external

_____

Conflict ___ internal ___ external

_____

Plot
Inciting incident _____

Climax _____

Resolution _____

_____

Themes _____

2. **Prewriting: Critical Essay, page 846.** Examine Bradamante and Ruggiero's relationship. Then compare and contrast Bradamante and Pinabello. Take notes on your findings. Using this information, make a rough outline of your essay in the space below. For more information on rough outlines, see the Language Arts Survey 1.12, "Outlining."

_____

_____

_____

_____

_____

_____

_____

_____

_____

_____

_____

_____

_____

_____

_____

_____

_____

_____

_____

_____

_____

_____

_____

_____

_____

_____

_____

_____

_____

_____

Selection Worksheet

10.3

Sonnet 23, page 847

READER RESPONSE ACTIVITIES

1. **Reader's Journal, page 848.** Think about a time when you were separated from somebody for whom you cared very deeply. On the lines below, write about the separation and how it made you feel. You may also wish to write about any emotions the other person may have expressed at the time.

_____

_____

_____

_____

_____

_____

2. **Guided Reading.** Answer these questions as you read the selection.

   Page 848: What did the person being addressed do long ago?

   _____

   _____

   Page 848: What does the speaker accuse her friend of trying to do to her?

   _____

3. **Responding to the Selection, page 849.** How would you react if the speaker of the poem were addressing you directly? Describe your reaction below. You may also wish to try to write a response in a verse of your own.

   _____

   _____

   _____

   _____

   _____

   _____

RESPONDING IN WRITING

1. **Prewriting: Couplet, page 850.** Freewrite about your chosen subject on the lines below. Then write a prose statement that summarizes your feelings. Experiment with the wording of this statement.

_____

_____

_____

_____

_____

_____

_____

Statement of feelings

_____

_____

_____

2. **Prewriting: Critical Essay, page 850.** First list and briefly explain Petrarchan ideals. Then note Labé's attitude toward each ideal.

PETRARCHAN IDEAL	LABÉ'S RESPONSE

Selection Worksheet

10.4

from *The Ingenious Hidalgo Don Quixote de la Mancha*, page 852

READER RESPONSE ACTIVITIES

1. **Reader's Journal, 853.** Have you ever read a book or seen a movie in which you wanted to take part? Think of a scene from one of these books or movies. Imagine yourself taking part in the scene. What part would you play? What would happen to you? Write about such a scene on the lines below.

_____

_____

_____

_____

_____

_____

_____

_____

_____

_____

_____

_____

2. **Guided Reading.** Answer these questions as you read the selection.

Page 853: What does Quixana like to do in his spare time? What becomes of this interest?

_____

_____

Page 854: What thoughts fill Quixana's imagination? What happens as he mulls over these thoughts?

_____

_____

Page 855: What does Quixana decide that he must do?

_____

_____

Page 855: What name does Quixana give his horse? Explain the significance of this name to Quixana. What makes this name humorous?

_____

_____

Page 855: What name does Quixana choose for himself? Why does he choose this name?

_____

_____

Page 856: Who is Dulcinea? Why does Don Quixote call her that?

_____

_____

Page 857: What foe does Don Quixote intend to fight? What is he really battling?

_____

_____

3. **Responding to the Selection, page 858.** Imagine that you are Don Quixote's neighbor. Describe what you think of his actions and his quest.

_____

_____

_____

_____

_____

_____

_____

_____

_____

_____

_____

_____

_____

_____

_____

RESPONDING IN WRITING

1. **Prewriting: Parody, page 859.** Do two focused freewrites. In the space below, freewrite about your superhero. What are his or her special strengths? For what qualities does he or she stand? Does he or she have any weaknesses? Then on your own paper, freewrite about ways in which your hero tries to prove something about himself or herself.

_____

_____

_____

_____

_____

_____

_____

_____

_____

_____

_____

_____

_____

_____

_____

_____

_____

_____

_____

_____

_____

_____

_____

_____

_____

2. **Prewriting: Critical Essay, page 859.** Begin by identifying aspects of a medieval romance. Next to each aspect that is parodied in the selection from *Don Quixote*, write a brief explanation of the way in which that aspect is satirized.

ASPECTS OF MEDIEVAL ROMANCE	SATIRE

Selection Worksheet

10.5

from "Of Cannibals," page 860

READER RESPONSE ACTIVITIES

1. **Reader's Journal, page 861.** Have you ever met somebody from a culture or background very different from your own? What aspects of this person's culture seemed especially unusual or interesting to you? What benefits do you see in learning about other cultures? Write about these questions on the lines below.

_____

_____

_____

_____

_____

_____

_____

_____

_____

_____

_____

_____

_____

2. **Guided Reading.** Answer these questions as you read the selection.

   Page 861: What do we call barbarism? What do people think of the place in which they live?

   _____

   _____

   Page 861: What is Montaigne's opinion about art in relation to nature?

   _____

   _____

   Page 862: What rules the people about whom Montaigne writes? What is Montaigne's opinion of the state of these people?

   _____

   _____

Page 863: What is the role of the prophet? Why is it important for the prophet to be correct?

_____

_____

Page 864: What faults are noted in others? According to Montaigne, to what barbarous practices of their own are Europeans blind?

_____

_____

Page 864: What do these people do with their prisoners?

_____

_____

Page 864: What treatment of prisoners did they learn from the Portuguese?

_____

_____

3. **Responding to the Selection, page 865.** Montaigne writes, "Each man calls barbarism whatever is not his own practice; for indeed it seems we have no other test of truth or reason than the example and pattern of the opinions and customs of the country we live in." Do you agree or disagree with this statement? Do you think that customs that differ from your own are strange or bad? Why, or why not?

_____

_____

_____

_____

_____

_____

_____

_____

_____

_____

_____

_____

Responding in Writing

1. **Prewriting: Personal Essay, page 866.** Gather ideas about your topic by using the cluster chart below. Fill in the center circle with the topic you have chosen. Then fill in the other circles with related ideas.

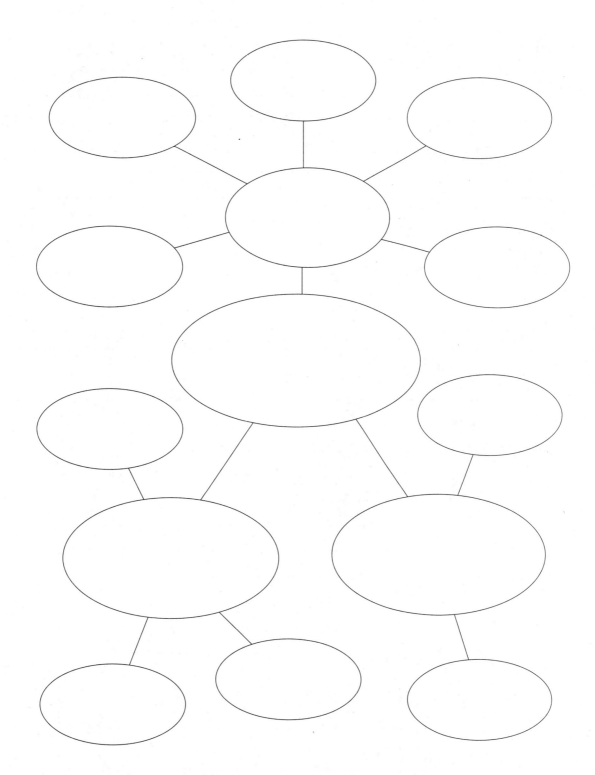

2. **Prewriting: Critical Essay, page 866.** Discuss your reaction to "Of Cannibals" with a peer to clarify your ideas. As you talk, jot down ideas that you may wish to use in your essay.

_____

_____

_____

_____

_____

_____

_____

_____

_____

_____

_____

_____

_____

_____

_____

_____

_____

_____

_____

_____

_____

_____

_____

_____

_____

_____

_____

_____

_____

_____

_____

Selection Worksheet

from *Fables*, page 867

READER RESPONSE ACTIVITIES

1. **Reader's Journal, page 868.** What morals or lessons were taught to you as a child in the form of aphorisms or short sayings? For example, you may have heard "Where there's a will, there's a way," or "Pride goes before a fall." List below as many morals or sayings as you can. Compare your list with those of your classmates, and discuss the meaning of each saying using concrete examples to illustrate it.

_____

_____

_____

_____

_____

_____

_____

_____

_____

_____

_____

_____

_____

_____

_____

_____

_____

_____

2. **Guided Reading.** Answer these questions as you read the selection.

   Page 868: What does the lion do for the rat?

   _____

   _____

   Page 868: In what way does the rat help the lion?

   _____

   _____

Page 869: What does the oak think of the reed?

_____

_____

Page 869: What quality does the reed recognize in itself? What weakness does it see in the oak?

_____

_____

3. **Responding to the Selection, page 870.** How would you feel at the end of "The Rat and the Lion" if you were the lion? How would you feel at the end of "The Oak and the Reed" if you were the oak? Describe the feelings and thoughts of either the lion or the oak on the lines below.

_____

_____

_____

_____

_____

_____

_____

_____

_____

_____

_____

_____

_____

_____

_____

_____

_____

_____

_____

RESPONDING IN WRITING

1. **Prewriting: Fable, page 871.** Write your moral in the space provided. Then do a focused freewrite about ways in which your moral might be illustrated.

Moral:

_____

_____

_____

Ways my moral might be illustrated:

_____

_____

_____

_____

_____

_____

_____

_____

_____

_____

_____

_____

_____

_____

_____

_____

_____

_____

_____

_____

_____

2. **Prewriting: Critical Essay, page 871.** After reviewing the selections by Ovid and by La Fontaine, complete the Venn diagram below. Address similarities and differences in tone, style, and theme.

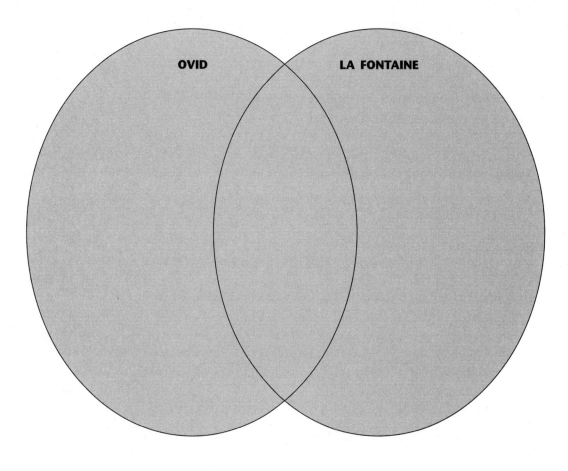

OVID

LA FONTAINE

Selection Worksheet

10.7

from *Tartuffe*, page 872

READER RESPONSE ACTIVITIES

1. **Reader's Journal, page 873.** Think of a time when someone deceived you. What did the person do to deceive you? How did you learn of the deception? How did you feel when the deception was revealed? Write about these questions on the lines below.

_____

_____

_____

_____

_____

_____

_____

_____

_____

_____

_____

_____

_____

_____

2. **Guided Reading.** Answer these questions as you read the selection.

Page 874: How does Mariane feel about marrying Tartuffe? What is her opinion of Tartuffe?

_____

_____

Page 874: Why doesn't Orgon believe what Elmire and Damis have told him about Tartuffe?

_____

_____

Page 874: What reason does Orgon give Mariane for going through with the marriage?

_____

_____

Page 876: What explanation does Elmire make to Orgon when he has hidden under the table? Why does she tell him this?

_____

_____

Page 877: Does Tartuffe believe Elmire's confession? What would make him more willing to believe her?

_____

_____

Page 878: What opinion does Tartuffe express about joy and dreams? What purpose lies behind this statement?

_____

_____

Page 878: What does Elmire suggest is an obstacle to their love? What does Tartuffe think of the obstacle that Elmire presents? What does he reveal about himself in these lines?

_____

_____

_____

Page 879: What is Tartuffe's opinion of Orgon? What might Orgon be thinking when he hears Tartuffe talk about him in this way?

_____

_____

Page 880: What problem has Orgon's blindness to Tartuffe's character caused?

_____

_____

3. **Responding to the Selection, page 881.** At the end of this selection do you feel sympathetic toward Orgon? Why, or why not? What are your feelings toward Tartuffe? Elmire? Do you think her anger toward her husband is justified?

_____

_____

_____

_____

_____

Name _____ Class _____ Date _____

_____

_____

_____

_____

_____

RESPONDING IN WRITING

1. **Prewriting: Diatribe, page 882.** Think about how Orgon feels about Tartuffe. You may wish to consider a time when you felt deceived by somebody. Freewrite to gather ideas for your diatribe focusing on feelings of deception.

_____

_____

_____

_____

_____

_____

_____

_____

_____

_____

_____

_____

_____

_____

_____

_____

_____

_____

_____

_____

2. **Prewriting: Critical Essay, page 882.** As you prepare to write this essay, respond to the following questions: Is the character or event satirical? Is something ironic about the event or about the character's actions? If so, explain. In what way does this character or event contribute to the overall effect of the act?

_____

_____

_____

_____

_____

_____

_____

_____

_____

_____

_____

_____

_____

_____

_____

_____

_____

_____

_____

_____

_____

_____

_____

_____

_____

Selection Worksheet

10.8

from *Candide*, page 884

READER RESPONSE ACTIVITIES

1. **Reader's Journal, page 885.** Are you an optimist or a pessimist? What is the difference between blind optimism and clear-sighted optimism? Do you agree or disagree with the statement that "This is the best of all possible worlds"? Explain your response in your journal.

_____

_____

_____

_____

_____

_____

_____

_____

_____

_____

_____

_____

_____

2. **Guided Reading.** Answer these questions as you read the selection.

   Page 885: What makes Candide's name fitting? Why might Voltaire have chosen such a name?

   _____

   _____

   Page 886: What philosophical views did Pangloss teach Candide?

   _____

   _____

   Page 886: What does Candide consider to be the four greatest happinesses?

   _____

   _____

Page 887: Why is Candide punished by the army? In what way is he allowed to exercise his "liberty"?

_____

_____

Page 888: What does Candide expect will happen in Holland?

_____

_____

Page 889: How does the "charity" orator respond to Candide's request for alms? How do his preachings correspond to his own actions?

_____

_____

Page 889: What state is Pangloss in when Candide meets him again? Can Pangloss's current condition be explained by his own philosophy?

_____

_____

3. **Responding to the Selection, page 890.** How would you feel upon meeting Pangloss again if you were Candide? Would you agree with Pangloss's assessment that this is the best of all possible worlds and that everything that happens is for the best possible end? Why, or why not?

_____

_____

_____

_____

_____

_____

_____

_____

_____

_____

_____

_____

_____

RESPONDING IN WRITING

1. **Prewriting: Description, page 891.** Fill in the cluster chart below with the problems that you perceive in the world that would not exist in a perfect world.

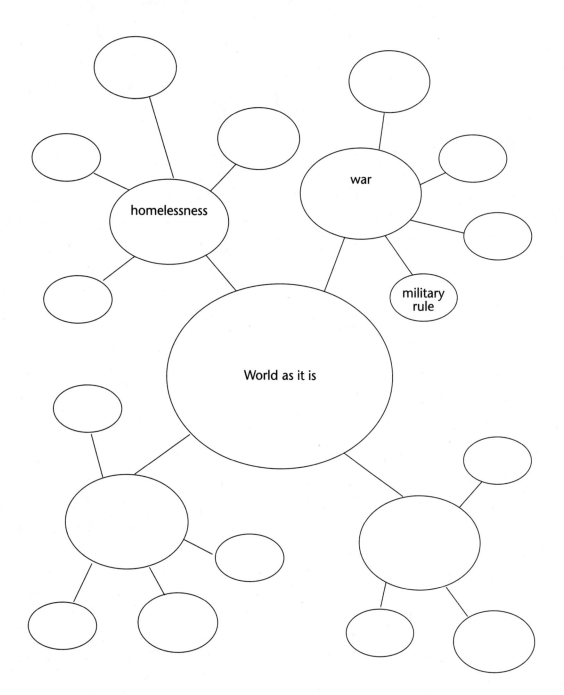

2. **Prewriting: Critical Essay, page 891.** First write a thesis statement critiquing Pangloss's philosophy. Then make a rough outline of the points you will use to support your case.

Thesis:

_____

_____

_____

_____

Outline:

_____

_____

_____

_____

_____

_____

_____

_____

_____

_____

_____

_____

_____

_____

_____

_____

_____

_____

_____

_____

_____

_____

Selection Worksheet

"My Heart Leaps Up When I Behold," page 904

READER RESPONSE ACTIVITIES

1. **Reader's Journal, page 905.** How do you feel when you observe a beautiful scene in the natural world? If such a scene has ever moved you, describe it along with the thoughts and feelings that it evoked. If you have never been moved by nature, explain why natural scenes do not evoke strong emotional reactions in you, and state what type of scene does inspire such a reaction in you.

_____

_____

_____

_____

_____

_____

_____

_____

_____

_____

_____

_____

_____

_____

_____

_____

_____

2. **Guided Reading.** Answer these questions as you read the selection.

   Page 905: What emotion does the speaker experience when he sees a rainbow?

   _____

   _____

   Page 905: By what does the speaker wish all his days to be bound?

   _____

   _____

3. **Responding to the Selection, page 906.** If you were about to take a long walk through a beautiful rural setting, would you want the speaker of this selection to come along? Explain why or why not.

_____

_____

_____

_____

_____

_____

_____

RESPONDING IN WRITING

1. **Prewriting: Paradoxes, page 907.** A paradox is a seemingly contradictory statement, idea, or event. Before you begin writing paradoxical statements, brainstorm a list of opposites, such as *beginning* and *end* or *parent* and *child*, in the space below.

_____   _____

_____   _____

_____   _____

_____   _____

_____   _____

2. **Prewriting: Critical Essay, page 907.** Use the chart below to organize ideas for your essay. First, write elements or defining characteristics of Romanticism in the left-hand column. Then find and record in the right-hand column examples from the poem that support or demonstrate each criteria from the left column.

ELEMENTS OF ROMANTICISM	"MY HEART LEAPS UP . . ."
Values or celebrates nature	

Selection Worksheet

11.2

"Loreley," page 909

READER RESPONSE ACTIVITIES

1. **Reader's Journal, page 910.** Think about a temptation you may have experienced to do something dangerous. Write about that situation. What was intriguing or appealing to you about the temptation? Did you think about the risks involved before you acted? What happened as a result of your actions? If you have not been in such a situation, or if you do not wish to write about such a situation, write about the effects temptation might have on a person's judgment.

_____

_____

_____

_____

_____

_____

_____

_____

2. **Guided Reading.** Answer these questions as you read the selection.

   Page 910: To what story does the speaker refer? What effect does the story have on the speaker?

   _____

   _____

   Page 910: At what time of day does the action of the poem take place?

   _____

   _____

   Page 910: What does the lovely maiden do?

   _____

   _____

   Page 911: What effect does the song of the Loreley have on the sailor?

   _____

   _____

3. Responding to the Selection, page 912. Has there ever been in your life a Loreley, or something that seemed wonderful but actually drove you to danger? How might you avoid the call of the Loreley? Freewrite about these questions.

_____

_____

_____

_____

_____

_____

RESPONDING IN WRITING

1. Prewriting: Song, page 913. First, think about the emotional effect you would like your song to have on the listener. Then, on the lines below, freewrite images that might create such a response.

_____

_____

_____

_____

_____

_____

2. Prewriting: Critical Essay, page 913. Reread the poem paying special attention to the language used to show the speaker's mood, the setting and time of day, the appearance and behavior of the Loreley, the effect of the Loreley's song on the sailor, and the effect of the tale of the Loreley on the speaker. Use the chart below to take notes as you read. Note in the left-hand column words and phrases that contribute to a specific tone, and in the right-hand column describe the effect.

ANALYSIS OF TONE IN "LORELEY"	
LANGUAGE USED	EFFECT

Selection Worksheet

from *Les Misérables*, page 914

READER RESPONSE ACTIVITIES

1. **Reader's Journal, page 915.** Have you ever known someone who, having been mistreated, returned kindness to the one who mistreated him or her? If so, describe the situation, and speculate about why this person was able to return kindness for cruelty. If you have not come across such a situation, speculate what might motivate a person to "turn the other cheek," or to be kind to someone who injured him or her.

_____

_____

_____

_____

_____

_____

_____

_____

2. **Guided Reading.** Answer these questions as you read the selection.

   Page 915: Does the bishop seem upset by the man's sudden entrance into his home?

   _____

   _____

   Page 915: What has the man who enters the room been doing?

   _____

   _____

   Page 915: Why might Madame Magloire be frightened by the man?

   _____

   _____

   Page 916: What does Jean Valjean suddenly understand? How does he feel about this situation? Why did he tell the bishop at once the worst about himself? What did he expect the bishop to do?

   _____

   _____

Page 916: Why do you think the woman directed Jean to the bishop's house?

_____

_____

Page 916: Why does Jean Valjean stop the bishop after he orders that a place at the table be set for Jean?

_____

_____

Page 917: How long did Jean work to earn this money? How do you think the bishop feels about the fact that Jean had to labor so long for so little?

_____

_____

Page 918: Why did the bishop let Jean in so readily? According to the bishop, to whom does his home really belong?

_____

_____

Page 918: Why didn't the bishop need to know Jean Valjean's name?

_____

_____

Page 918: How does Jean feel when the bishop calls him *sir*? To what does the narrator compare the worth of a title of respect to a convict?

_____

_____

Page 918: According to the priest, in what does heaven rejoice?

_____

_____

Page 919: What are the two abysses between which Jean is hesitating?

_____

_____

Page 919: What does the bishop note is missing? What is the bishop trying to show Jean Valjean?

_____

_____

Page 919: What does the crucifix seem to be doing in the moonlight?

_____

_____

Page 919: What does Jean decide not to do? What does he decide to do?

_____

_____

Page 920: Why doesn't the bishop mind that the silver is missing?

_____

_____

Page 920: What is the bishop's attitude toward the missing silver? What does Madame Magloire think of his reaction?

_____

_____

Page 920: What does Madame Magloire think of the bishop's attitude toward Jean Valjean?

_____

_____

Page 921: What is the bishop's surprising response to the captured thief?

_____

_____

Page 921: What does Jean Valjean finally realize about the man who sheltered him?

_____

_____

Page 922: What is Jean's reaction to the bishop's surprising words?

_____

_____

Page 922: What does the bishop give to Jean?

_____

_____

Page 922: What does the bishop say that Jean must use the money from the silver to do? What has the bishop "bought" from Jean? What does he plan to do with this thing?

_____

_____

3. **Responding to the Selection, page 923.** What do you think of Jean Valjean? What is your opinion of Jean Valjean's behavior? Do you think that he will take the bishop's advice to heart and try to become an "honest man"?

_____

_____

_____

_____

_____

RESPONDING IN WRITING

1. **Prewriting: Personal Letter, page 924.** Before you write your letter to the bishop, take some time to freewrite about various situations in which Jean Valjean might find himself next. Use the space below to start, and continue on your own paper if you need more room.

_____

_____

_____

_____

2. **Prewriting: Critical Essay, page 924.** To complete the chart below, first fill in the characteristics of each movement in the first column. Then as you review the selection, list evidence that shows how the selection exhibits elements of each movement in the second column. Use the information in the chart as you construct your thesis and draft your essay.

MOVEMENT	EVIDENCE FROM SELECTION
Romanticism	
Realism	
Naturalism	

Selection Worksheet

11.4

"They say that plants don't talk . . . ," page 925

READER RESPONSE ACTIVITIES

1. **Reader's Journal, page 926.** Choose two or three natural images. Describe these images in detail. In what ways do these images "speak" to you? In other words, in what way do these aspects of nature affect you?

   _____

   _____

   _____

   _____

   _____

   _____

   _____

2. **Guided Reading.** Answer these questions as you read the selection.

   Page 926: What do people say about plants, brooks, birds, waves, and stars? Why doesn't the speaker agree?

   _____

   _____

   Page 926: What does the speaker call herself? About what does she dream?

   _____

   _____

   _____

   Page 927: Why must nature stop gossiping about the speaker's dreams?

   _____

   _____

3. **Responding to the Selection, page 928.** If you were a friend of the speaker of this poem and happened to meet her after one of her walks through the woods, what might she tell you about the importance that nature has for her? What might she say to describe her feelings about life?

   _____

   _____

_____

_____

_____

_____

_____

RESPONDING IN WRITING

1. **Prewriting: Personification, page 929.** On your own paper, brainstorm a list of elements of nature. Choose one to explore more closely. Then, in the space below, do a focused freewrite about the element you chose. Imagine that your element is a person and answer some of the following questions: What activities would it enjoy? What would its voice sound like? In what manner would it move or what movements would it enjoy? What qualities or beliefs would it embrace?

_____

_____

_____

_____

_____

_____

_____

_____

_____

2. **Prewriting: Critical Essay, page 929.** Review the poem and try to answer the following questions: What does nature mean to the speaker? In what way does she communicate with nature? In what way does she relate elements of nature to aspects of her own life? Write your responses to the questions below, and when possible, include line references to the parts of the poem that support your response.

_____

_____

_____

_____

_____

_____

_____

Selection Worksheet

from *Germinal,* page 930

READER RESPONSE ACTIVITIES

1. **Reader's Journal, page 931.** Imagine that you are an adult and that you suddenly lose your job. Times are hard, and you have difficulty finding new work right away. If you were in this position, what fears and concerns would you have? What would you do to get back on your feet again? Respond to these questions on the lines below.

_____

_____

_____

_____

_____

_____

_____

_____

_____

_____

_____

_____

_____

2. **Guided Reading.** Answer these questions as you read the selection.

   Page 931: At what time of day and in what weather conditions is the man journeying?

   _____

   _____

   Page 931: What single thought occupies the man? What does he see that might fulfill his needs? Is this a long term solution to his problem?

   _____

   _____

   Page 932: What does the carman tell Étienne? What strange thing interrupts their conversation?

   _____

   _____

Page 932: What does the man see when he approaches the fires? Why does his despair return?

_____

_____

_____

Page 932: Whom does the man address? What is this person doing?

_____

_____

Page 932: Who is the man who addresses the old carman? What does he do for a living? What is he seeking? What is his physical appearance?

_____

_____

_____

Page 933: To what does Étienne compare the coal pit?

_____

_____

Page 933: How long has Étienne been out of work? Why was he fired from his last job?

_____

_____

Page 934: What has been happening in Montsou?

_____

_____

Page 934: About what issues do the men complain?

_____

_____

Page 935: How long has Bonnemort worked at the mines? When did he start?

_____

_____

Page 935: What is the old carman called? Why did others give him this nickname?

_____

_____

Page 936: What do the people who manage the mine want Bonnemort to do? Why won't he do this?

_____

_____

Page 937: What does Bonnemort cough up?

_____

_____

Page 937: In what way does the financial state of the mining company contrast with the financial state of its workers?

_____

_____

Page 937: What happened to Bonnemort's father, uncles, and brothers in the mine? Why does Bonnemort's family continue to work there?

_____

_____

Page 938: What does Étienne resolve? What doubt troubles him?

_____

_____

Page 938: To what does the narrator compare Bonnemort's attitude toward the mine's owners?

_____

_____

Page 938: What does the mine appear to be doing to the miners who are descending into it?

_____

_____

3. **Responding to the Selection, page 938.** If you were in Étienne's position, would you take a job at the Voreaux? Explain what factors would influence your decision.

_____

_____

_____

_____

_____

_____

_____

_____

_____

RESPONDING IN WRITING

1. **Prewriting: Social Critique, page 940.** With a partner or in a small group, discuss one or more issues that interest you. Address the effects of the social condition you choose, different opinions on the issue, and possible solutions. During your discussion, jot down notes about important ideas that you want to use in your critique.

_____

_____

_____

_____

_____

_____

_____

_____

_____

2. **Prewriting: Critical Essay, page 940.** Use the analysis chart below to gather evidence for your essay. In the first column, list actions or decisions of characters in the selection. In the second column, explain how the item in the first column is related to Naturalism.

ACTIONS OR DECISIONS	RELATIONSHIP TO NATURALISM

Selection Worksheet

11.6

"The False Gems," page 941

READER RESPONSE ACTIVITIES

1. **Reader's Journal, page 942.** Describe a time when something happened to change completely your image of a person or a situation. What image had been in your mind? What happened to change this image? How did the image change? How did you feel when this happened? Was it a positive or negative experience? Why?

_____

_____

_____

_____

_____

_____

_____

_____

_____

_____

_____

_____

_____

2. **Guided Reading.** Answer these questions as you read the selection.

Page 942: What had the young woman's mother hoped to do? What words does the narrator use to describe the young woman's family?

_____

_____

Page 942: For what two things does M. Lantin blame his wife?

_____

_____

Page 942: What do people never tire of saying about the young woman? What does M. Lantin do?

_____

_____

Page 943: What does M. Lantin beg his wife to do? What is her response to this request?

_____

_____

Page 943: What happens to M. Lantin's wife?

_____

_____

Page 943: What happens to M. Lantin's financial situation after his wife's death? What does he wonder about his wife's ability to handle financial matters? What does desperation drive him to do?

_____

_____

_____

Page 943: In what way does the young woman look at her gems?

_____

_____

Page 944: How does M. Lantin feel about the false gems? What effect does the sight of them have on him?

_____

_____

Page 945: What kind of person does the second jeweler believe M. Lantin to be?

_____

_____

Page 945: What does M. Lantin realize about the necklace and all the other jewels in his wife's possession? What question is in his mind?

_____

_____

Page 945: How has learning his wife's secret made him feel?

_____

_____

Page 945: What does M. Lantin decide as he observes the men of leisure?

_____

_____

Page 946: After receiving money for the necklace, what does M. Lantin decide to do with the other gems? What does he learn about them?

_____

_____

Page 946: In what way does M. Lantin's life change when he first inherits his fortune? What does he do to change his situation? What kind of person does he marry?

_____

_____

_____

3. **Responding to the Selection, page 947.** Imagine that you are M. Lantin. How would you feel after finding out the secret of the "false gems"? What questions might be in your own mind?

_____

_____

_____

_____

_____

_____

_____

_____

_____

_____

_____

_____

_____

_____

_____

_____

RESPONDING IN WRITING

1. **Prewriting: Observation and Description, page 948.** First, as you examine the picture you have chosen, jot down key words and phrases that describe the picture. Include descriptions of the appearance of people and objects, apparent emotions of people, actions, and placement of things in the picture in relation to one another.

_____

_____

_____

_____

_____

_____

_____

_____

_____

_____

_____

_____

_____

_____

_____

_____

_____

_____

_____

_____

_____

2. **Prewriting: Critical Essay, page 948.** After reading both selections, complete the chart below. In the first column, list a similarity you note in the two works. Then in the next two columns identify examples from the two selections that support your claim.

SIMILARITY	MAUPASSANT	FLAUBERT

Selection Worksheet

"The Bet," page 949

READER RESPONSE ACTIVITIES

1. **Reader's Journal, page 950.** Imagine that you were placed in solitary confinement for five years. You are allowed to read, to write, to play or listen to music, and you are provided with whatever food you wish. How would you spend your time? What might you think about? What would you miss most? Write your responses to these questions in your journal. You might write several entries that show your feelings during different periods of your confinement.

_____

_____

_____

_____

_____

_____

_____

_____

_____

_____

_____

_____

2. **Guided Reading.** Answer these questions as you read the selection.

   Page 950: What topic does the banker remember discussing fifteen years earlier? What opinion on the issue had the banker expressed?

   _____

   _____

   Page 950: What opinion does the young lawyer express? What wager does the banker offer? What do you think of the lawyer's decision to accept the bet?

   _____

   _____

   _____

Page 951: How have the banker's feelings about the bet changed in the fifteen years since it was made? What do you think caused this change of feeling?

_____

_____

Page 951: With what activities does the prisoner fill his first year? What does he do differently the second year? In what way has his attitude changed?

_____

_____

_____

Page 951: Explain the conditions of the contract. What will the lawyer be allowed to do? What will he not be allowed to do?

_____

_____

_____

Page 952: What does the prisoner do during his sixth year of confinement? What request does he make of his jailer? What is his opinion of humankind based on his studies of philosophy and history?

_____

_____

_____

Page 953: What does the banker see as his only hope? What does he intend to do?

_____

_____

Page 953: Describe the prisoner's reading habits during the last two years of his confinement. To what does the narrator compare the prisoner's reading? What does this comparison suggest about the prisoner's state of mind during the last two years?

_____

_____

_____

Page 953: On the day before the terms of the bet will be completed, what is troubling the banker? What change in circumstances has he undergone during the last fifteen years?

_____

_____

Page 954: What effect has confinement had on the lawyer physically?

_____

_____

Page 954: How has the man's opinion of the world changed from his opinion before his confinement? from the opinion he held during his early years of confinement?

_____

_____

_____

Page 955: After reading the letter, how does the banker feel about himself? about his situation?

_____

_____

3. **Responding to the Selection, page 956.** What kind of life do you think the lawyer will lead, now that he has left his confinement? What is his attitude toward life? How might this attitude affect his relationships with others? Are you sympathetic toward this character? Why, or why not?

_____

_____

_____

_____

_____

_____

_____

_____

_____

_____

_____

_____

_____

_____

_____

_____

RESPONDING IN WRITING

1. **Prewriting: Interview, page 957.** Using the prompts below write six questions to ask the lawyer. On your own paper, freewrite about each response separately before writing an answer.

Who _____ ?

What _____ ?

When _____ ?

Where _____ ?

Why _____ ?

How do you feel about _____

_____ ?

2. **Prewriting: Critical Essay, page 957.** Review the story, taking notes on your own paper about passages that support your opinion of the lawyer. Then in the space below, make a rough outline of your essay.

_____

_____

_____

_____

_____

_____

_____

_____

_____

_____

_____

_____

_____

_____

_____

_____

_____

_____

_____

_____

Selection Worksheet

from *Cyrano de Bergerac*, page 958

READER RESPONSE ACTIVITIES

1. **Reader's Journal, page 959.** Imagine that two people are in love with you. The first person is not physically beautiful but is very entertaining, intelligent, and imaginative. The second person is outwardly beautiful but foolish and boring. Whom would you choose? Explain why.

_____

_____

_____

_____

_____

_____

_____

_____

_____

_____

_____

_____

_____

_____

2. **Guided Reading.** Answer these questions as you read the selection.

Page 959: What might one easily do?

_____

_____

Page 960: What are the duenna and Roxane planning to attend?

_____

_____

Page 961: How did Cyrano acquire the pair of musicians?

_____

_____

Page 962: Why has Cyrano come?

_____

_____

Page 962: What does Roxane love about Christian?

_____

_____

Page 962: Of what does Roxane accuse Cyrano?

_____

_____

Page 963: What does Cyrano say about the writing in general? What does he say when he learns that Roxane has memorized the lines?

_____

_____

_____

Page 963: How does Roxane feel about De Guiche's love for her?

_____

_____

Page 963: How does Roxane feel about the thought of De Guiche leaving to go to war?

_____

_____

Page 964: How does Roxane feel when she learns that Christian is also going off to war? How does De Guiche interpret her reaction?

_____

_____

_____

Page 965: What does Roxane try to convince De Guiche to do? Why does she do this?

_____

_____

Page 965: In what way does De Guiche interpret Roxane's plan?

_____

_____

Page 966: What has Roxane accomplished by pretending to side with De Guiche in his dispute with Cyrano?

_____

_____

Page 966: Why does Roxane pretend to love De Guiche?

_____

_____

Page 966: How does Roxane think Cyrano would feel if he knew what she has done?

_____

_____

Page 967: What does Cyrano tell Christian to do?

_____

_____

Page 968: What doesn't Christian want to do anymore? Why doesn't he want to do this?

_____

_____

Page 968: What does Christian decide once he sees Roxane? What does Cyrano do? Why?

_____

_____

_____

Page 968: How does Roxane react to Christian's words of love when he speaks without Cyrano's help?

_____

_____

Page 970: To what does Roxane compare Christian's lack of eloquence?

_____

_____

Page 970: Why does Roxane shut the door in Christian's face? To whom does Christian turn for help?

_____

_____

Page 971: For what purpose does Cyrano use the musicians?

_____

_____

Page 971: Why does Roxane believe that Christian does not love her anymore?

_____

_____

Page 971: How does Christian know what to say to woo Roxane?

_____

_____

Page 972: What does Roxane notice? What is the real reason for this?

_____

_____

Page 972: What does Cyrano decide to do?

_____

_____

Page 972: What explanation does Cyrano provide for his hesitation to come closer? What do you think Roxane's reaction would be if Cyrano did allow himself to be seen?

_____

_____

_____

Page 973: What does Cyrano almost admit?

_____

_____

Page 974: According to Cyrano, why should Roxane be more concerned with enjoying love in her life than with hearing it expressed in poetry?

_____

_____

Page 975: What does Cyrano say he is giving Roxane? What does he want in return? Is Cyrano speaking for Christian or for himself?

_____

_____

_____

Page 976: What makes Cyrano happy enough to die satisfied?

_____

_____

Page 976: Why does Christian interrupt Cyrano? What reason does he provide for his actions?

_____

_____

Page 977: What is Cyrano's real reason for refusing to win Christian a kiss?

_____

_____

Page 977: What reason does Cyrano provide for all his aid to Christian in his pursuit of Roxane?

_____

_____

Page 978: How do you think that Cyrano feels about Christian claiming a kiss from Roxane?

_____

_____

Page 979: What does Cyrano say that Christian is doing by kissing Roxane?

_____

_____

Page 979: Why has De Guiche written a letter to Roxane?

_____

_____

Page 980: What does Roxane say the purpose of the letter is?

_____

_____

3. **Responding to the Selection, page 981.** Imagine that you are Roxane. What would your reaction be to the proclamation of love Cyrano delivers for Christian? How would you feel toward Cyrano if you knew that the words were his own? How would you feel toward Christian?

_____

_____

_____

_____

_____

_____

_____

RESPONDING IN WRITING

1. **Prewriting: Dramatic Continuation, page 983.** In small groups, role play several possible endings to the play. Choose the ending that you prefer from those you improvised, and jot down some ideas about the best possible ending in the space below.

_____

_____

_____

_____

_____

_____

_____

_____

_____

_____

2. **Prewriting: Critical Essay, page 983.** The analysis chart below will help you to organize your ideas for your critical essay. As you reread Cyrano's speech which begins on page 975 ("Yes, that is Love—that wind"), write the number(s) of the line or line(s) you are examining in the first column. Then in the second column note the relationship of the line or lines to Cyrano's situation.

LINE(S)	RELATIONSHIP TO CYRANO'S SITUATION

Selection Worksheet

"The Shoes," page 984

READER RESPONSE ACTIVITIES

1. **Reader's Journal, page 985.** Do you think you have control over your life, or do you think of it as controlled by outside forces? Think about a time when something bad happened or when you were dissatisfied with your life. How did you react? Did you blame yourself or forces outside your control? Respond to these questions on the lines below.

_____

_____

_____

_____

_____

_____

_____

_____

_____

_____

_____

_____

_____

_____

_____

2. **Guided Reading.** Answer these questions as you read the selection.

   Page 985: What is Elia Carái's profession? How is business lately? What does he do when he does not have any cases?

   _____

   _____

   Page 985: What does Elia know about the world? What does he hope will happen? Describe his philosophy of life.

   _____

   _____

Page 986: How does Elia's wife act? In what way are her actions similar to his? What does this type of behavior suggest about Elia and his wife?

_____

_____

_____

Page 986: Why do matters take a turn for the worse? How does Elia accept this turn of events? Why is this problem troubling to him?

_____

_____

_____

Page 987: What does Elia imagine as he tries to sleep? Why is he so preoccupied with these things?

_____

_____

Page 988: Why is Elia on the floor? How does he feel when he hears a noise and fears he might be discovered?

_____

_____

Page 988: Describe the effect the shoes have on Elia. Why might he have this reaction to the shoes?

_____

_____

Page 988: What observation does Elia make as he leaves the inn? In what way is this observation related to his own situation?

_____

_____

Page 988: Why do you think the landscape now appears differently to Elia?

_____

_____

Page 989: What does Elia imagine happening? What do these imaginings suggest about his state of mind?

_____

_____

Page 989: What does Elia learn when he arrives at his uncle's house? How do you think Elia feels?

_____

_____

Page 989: What decision does Elia make? Do you think his decision is wise? Explain.

_____

_____

3. **Responding to the Selection, page 990.** What do you think the rest of life will be like for Elia and his wife? What advice would you give them about their situation?

_____

_____

_____

_____

_____

_____

_____

_____

_____

_____

_____

_____

_____

_____

RESPONDING IN WRITING

1. **Prewriting: Personal Philosophy, page 991.** With a partner discuss the following questions: How do you deal with problems or difficulties? What advice have you been given about how to live your life? What decisions have you made about what is important? What advice would you like to give others? As you talk about these questions, take notes in the space provided.

_____

_____

_____

_____

_____

_____

_____

_____

_____

_____

_____

_____

2. **Prewriting: Naturalism, page 991.** Before you begin this essay question, first define Naturalism. Then consider how the following aspects of the story might fit into the tenets of Naturalism: Elia's financial state, his attitude or philosophy of life, the actions he takes, and the events that spark these actions. Use the space below to answer these questions, continuing on your own paper if necessary.

Definition of Naturalism: _____

_____

Relating elements of the story to Naturalist beliefs:

_____

_____

_____

_____

_____

_____

_____

_____

_____

_____

_____

_____

_____

_____

_____

_____

_____

_____

_____

_____

Selection Worksheet

"Araby," page 1018

READER RESPONSE ACTIVITIES

1. **Reader's Journal, page 1019.** Describe a time when you experienced strong feelings, such as love, anger, or frustration, toward a person. Why did you have these feelings? How did these feelings affect your behavior, or your opinion about yourself?

   _____

   _____

   _____

   _____

   _____

   _____

   _____

   _____

2. **Guided Reading.** Answer these questions as you read the selection.

   Page 1019: What season does the narrator describe? What activities filled the narrator's afternoons?

   _____

   _____

   Page 1019: Who had been a former tenant in the narrator's house? What was the air like in the narrator's home?

   _____

   _____

   Page 1020: What does the narrator imagine? How might this be related to his feelings for Mangan's sister?

   _____

   _____

   Page 1020: What does the narrator do each morning, when he sees his friend Mangan's sister? Why does he do this?

   _____

   _____

Page 1020: What feelings does the narrator have for Mangan's sister? What does he murmur to himself?

_____

_____

Page 1020: What were Mangan's sister's first words to the narrator?

_____

_____

Page 1021: What does the narrator promise to do for Mangan's sister?

_____

_____

Page 1022: Of what does the speaker remind his uncle? In what tone of voice does the uncle respond?

_____

_____

Page 1022: Why might the narrator have to miss the bazaar?

_____

_____

Page 1022: How does the narrator get to the bazaar? At what time does he arrive?

_____

_____

Page 1023: What does the young lady ask the narrator? What does the narrator sense about the way she speaks to him?

_____

_____

Page 1023: When the narrator finally gets to the bazaar, how does he know that it is almost over?

_____

_____

Page 1023: What does a voice call out? How does the narrator feel as he gazes into the darkness?

_____

_____

3. **Responding to the Selection, page 1023.** Imagine that you are on the train with the narrator of this story, both as he travels to the bazaar and then as he travels home. What might he say about his expectations as he travels to the bazaar? On the way home, what might he say about his brief experience?

_____

_____

_____

_____

_____

_____

_____

_____

_____

_____

_____

_____

_____

_____

_____

_____

RESPONDING IN WRITING

1. **Prewriting: Childhood Memory, page 1025.** In the space below, freewrite to gather writing topics. If you have already chosen a particular memory, do a focused freewrite about the memory to gather details.

_____

_____

_____

_____

_____

_____

_____

_____

_____

_____

2. **Prewriting: Critical Essay, page 1025.** First answer the following questions:

What is the mood in the opening paragraphs of the piece?

_____

_____

_____

_____

When does the mood begin to change?

_____

_____

_____

_____

What is the mood at the end of the story?

_____

_____

_____

_____

Then complete the following plot pyramid. Next to each element, identify a related event from "Araby" and note the mood.

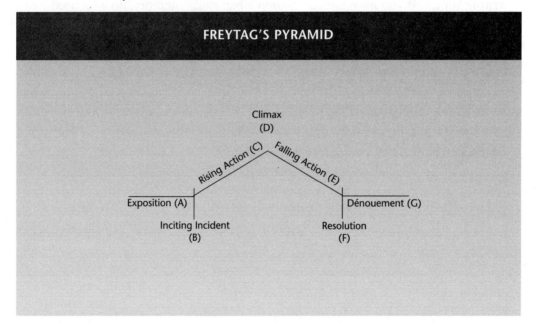

FREYTAG'S PYRAMID

Climax
(D)

Rising Action (C)   Falling Action (E)

Exposition (A)   Dénouement (G)

Inciting Incident   Resolution
(B)   (F)

© 1998 EMC Corporation

Selection Worksheet

12.2

from *Orlando*, page 1026

READER RESPONSE ACTIVITIES

1. **Reader's Journal, page 1027.** Do you believe in love at first sight? Based on your own experiences and what you have seen in movies, television, books, and popular song, explain on the lines below whether you believe love at first sight is possible. In what way might a relationship based on love at first sight be different from a relationship developed more slowly out of friendship or shared experiences and values?

   _____

   _____

   _____

   _____

   _____

   _____

   _____

   _____

2. **Guided Reading.** Answer these questions as you read the selection.

   Page 1027: What do historians tell us? What happens during this period? Do these events seem more like history or fantasy?

   _____

   _____

   Page 1027: What is the time of the Great Frost like for country people? What is the king's response to this disaster?

   _____

   _____

   Page 1027: What happens to some of the people who have been frozen stiff? To what uses do the English people put these unfortunate victims' remains?

   _____

   _____

Page 1028: What is unusual about the ice in the river?

_____

_____

Page 1028: What do philosophers wonder about the frozen fish?

_____

_____

Page 1028: What does King James especially enjoy about the frost?

_____

_____

Page 1029: What comes to Orlando's mind when he sees the mysterious person?

_____

_____

Page 1030: Why can't the English communicate with the Muscovites?

_____

_____

Page 1030: Why does the Muscovite princess put the English lords in a "predicament"?

_____

_____

Page 1030: What is Orlando doing mentally while gazing at the princess? What interrupts his thoughts?

_____

_____

Page 1030: Why do you think the narrator says that it would have been better for Orlando never to have learned French?

_____

_____

Page 1030: What do the English lords do in response to the princess's attempts to make conversation? What is her response?

_____

_____

© 1998 EMC Corporation

Page 1030: How does Orlando feel about his former loves now?

_____

_____

Page 1031: What does the princess really think of the English court?

_____

_____

3. **Responding to the Selection, page 1032.** What do you think of King James's winter carnival? If you were the leader in charge of England, what would your reaction to the Great Frost have been? What do you think of the English nobility as they are characterized in this selection from *Orlando?*

_____

_____

_____

_____

_____

_____

_____

_____

_____

_____

_____

_____

_____

_____

_____

_____

RESPONDING IN WRITING

1. **Prewriting: Biography, page 1034.** To gather information about your subject, conduct an interview with the person you are writing about or with other people who know your subject well. On the lines below, write several questions you might ask in an interview.

_____

_____

_____

_____

_____

_____

_____

_____

_____

_____

_____

_____

_____

_____

_____

_____

_____

_____

_____

2. **Prewriting: Critical Essay, page 1034.** Review the selection, taking notes about the use of realism and fantasy. Then use the outline form below to organize your ideas and the information you have gathered. Use your own paper to continue your outline if necessary.

I. _____

    A. _____

        1. _____

        2. _____

    B. _____

        1. _____

        2. _____

II. _____

    A. _____

        1. _____

        2. _____

    B. _____

        1. _____

        2. _____

Selection Worksheet

12.3

"The Guitar," page 1035

READER RESPONSE ACTIVITIES

1. **Reader's Journal, page 1036.** When was the last time that you felt really sad or hurt? What caused your sadness? Did a person or the outcome of an event disappoint you? How did you deal with your feelings of sadness? On the lines below, describe the experience.

_____

_____

_____

_____

_____

_____

_____

_____

_____

_____

_____

2. **Guided Reading.** Answer these questions as you read the selection.

   Page 1036: When does the crying of the guitar begin?

   _____

   _____

   Page 1036: What other things besides the guitar weep?

   _____

   _____

   Page 1036: Why does the guitar cry?

   _____

   _____

   Page 1036: How is the heart wounded?

   _____

   _____

3. **Responding to the Selection, page 1037.** What sort of music inspires strong feelings of sadness in you? Write about this music and its effect on you on the lines below.

_____

_____

_____

_____

_____

RESPONDING IN WRITING

1. **Prewriting: Free-Verse Poem, page 1039.** Choose an emotion. In the space below do a focused freewrite about this emotion. Try to think of the characteristics of this emotion and of things that might represent this emotion. Continue freewriting on your own paper if necessary. Then review your freewrite to find ideas for your poem.

_____

_____

_____

_____

_____

_____

2. **Prewriting: Critical Essay, page 1039.** Review the poem and answer the following questions.

Does the poem create one consistent mood?

_____

_____

If the mood changes, where does it change?

_____

_____

Why does it change?

_____

_____

What words and phrases help to create each mood in the poem?

_____

_____

Selection Worksheet

"And We Shall Be Steeped," page 1040

READER RESPONSE ACTIVITIES

1. **Reader's Journal, page 1041.** Do you think cultural traditions are important, or do you think they are outdated? On the lines below, write your opinions about your cultural heritage and the role it plays in your life. You might also write about the attitudes you perceive others have about your heritage.

   _____

   _____

   _____

   _____

   _____

2. **Guided Reading.** Answer these questions as you read the selection.

   Page 1041: In what will the speaker be steeped? How do you think the speaker feels about this presence?

   _____

   _____

   Page 1041: What symbols of the past are mentioned? What is the speaker's attitude toward the past?

   _____

   _____

   Page 1041: According to the speaker, what will the lamp do?

   _____

   _____

3. **Responding to the Selection, page 1042.** What attitudes toward, or impressions of, Africa do you have after reading this poem?

   _____

   _____

   _____

   _____

   _____

Responding in Writing

1. **Prewriting: Occasional Poem or Speech, page 1043.** To gather ideas for your occasional poem or speech, fill in the cluster chart below. Begin by writing the name of the place you have chosen as your subject in the center circle. Then fill in the other circles with things you associate with this place. Add more circles as necessary.

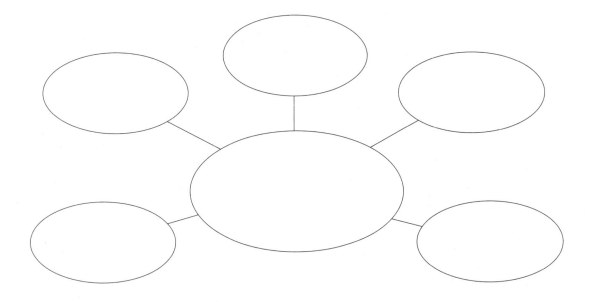

2. **Prewriting: Critical Essay, page 1043.** First make sure you understand the key elements of the Negritude movement. List these elements in the left column of the chart below. Then fill in the right column with examples or elements of "And We Shall Be Steeped" that correspond to each item in the left hand column.

NEGRITUDE MOVEMENT	"AND WE SHALL BE STEEPED"
_____	_____
_____	_____
_____	_____
_____	_____
_____	_____
_____	_____
_____	_____
_____	_____

Selection Worksheet

12.5

"Metonymy, or The Husband's Revenge," page 1044

READER RESPONSE ACTIVITIES

1. **Reader's Journal, page 1045.** Have you ever blamed somebody, not because of what he or she has done, but because this person is associated with something that makes you unhappy or angry? For example, have you ever been angry at a family member who gave you some bad news or been annoyed with a slow driver or people in a long line because you are running late? Think about one such situation, and write about it on the lines below. Describe your reaction to the situation and to the person involved.

_____

_____

_____

_____

_____

_____

_____

_____

_____

_____

_____

_____

_____

_____

_____

2. **Guided Reading.** Answer these questions as you read the selection.

   Page 1045: What word does the narrator say she learned in 1930? What example of this figure of speech had she used?

   _____

   _____

   Page 1045: In the first example of applied metonymy given by the narrator, why does the woman leave the boardinghouse?

   _____

   _____

Page 1045: What is metonymy? What classic example of this figure of speech does the narrator's professor provide?

_____

_____

Page 1046: Why might the man have had trouble finding a wife? Why was he able to find a woman to marry?

_____

_____

Page 1046: What did the woman whom the shopkeeper married look like? What effect did her change of lifestyle have? How did she feel about her husband as her appearance changed?

_____

_____

_____

_____

Page 1047: To what is the love of the shopkeeper's wife and the sergeant compared?

_____

_____

Page 1048: How does Fate feel about illicit love? What happens to the sergeant?

_____

_____

Page 1048: When does the shopkeeper begin to suspect his wife's affair? Why does he become suspicious?

_____

_____

Page 1048: Where does the wife keep her love letters? What had her husband told her about this place?

_____

_____

Page 1049: What reasons does the shopkeeper give for his inability to kill his wife?

_____

_____

Page 1049: Whom does the police chief think the shopkeeper has killed? Whom has he killed? Why did he kill this person?

_____

_____

3. **Responding to the Selection, page 1050.** Were you surprised by the end of the story? If you were surprised by the ending, describe what you thought would happen and why you thought this event would occur. If you were not surprised, identify your reasons for expecting the ending.

_____

_____

_____

_____

_____

_____

_____

_____

_____

_____

_____

_____

_____

_____

_____

_____

_____

_____

_____

_____

_____

_____

_____

RESPONDING IN WRITING

1. **Prewriting: Anecdote, page 1051.** After choosing an experience, freewrite about it. Try to gather a variety of concrete details that you can use in relating your anecdote.

_____

_____

_____

_____

_____

_____

_____

_____

_____

_____

_____

_____

_____

_____

2. **Prewriting: Critical Essay, page 1051.** Review the story, taking notes on examples of foreshadowing and irony. Then before you begin writing, make a rough outline of your essay in the space below.

_____

_____

_____

_____

_____

_____

_____

_____

_____

_____

_____

_____

_____

_____

Selection Worksheet

"The Myth of Sisyphus," page 1052

READER RESPONSE ACTIVITIES

1. **Reader's Journal, page 1053.** What activity or task in your life do you find most boring or meaningless? On the lines below, write your thoughts about performing this activity. What would your response be to someone who claimed that you should find joy in this task?

_____

_____

_____

_____

_____

_____

_____

_____

_____

_____

_____

_____

_____

_____

_____

2. **Guided Reading.** Answer these questions as you read the selection.

Page 1053: Why do the gods think that repeatedly rolling a rock to the top of a mountain, only to watch it roll back down again, is a suitable punishment for Sisyphus?

_____

_____

Page 1053: Why does Sisyphus leave the underworld and return to earth? What happens when he gets there?

_____

_____

Page 1053: What secret does Sisyphus give away? What deal does he make with Æsopus?

_____

_____

Page 1054: What happens when Mercury snatches Sisyphus away from earth?

_____

_____

Page 1054: What "unspeakable penalty" does Sisyphus's "scorn of the gods, his hatred of death, and his passion for life" win him?

_____

_____

Page 1055: What thoughts and images make Sisyphus's task more melancholy? How, on the other hand, might "crushing truths" be made to perish?

_____

_____

Page 1055: For what does Oedipus, with his remark, give a recipe? What does his ancient wisdom confirm?

_____

_____

Page 1055: Why is the myth of Sisyphus tragic? In what way is the average working person's fate just as absurd as the fate of Sisyphus? Why, at the same time, is the fate of the average working person far less tragic?

_____

_____

_____

Page 1055: According to the speaker, why is the remark of Oedipus sacred? What does it make of fate?

_____

_____

Page 1056: Why can Sisyphus find joy in his fate? Why, then, can the average person find joy in an "absurd" existence?

_____

_____

Page 1056: What is enough to fill a person's heart? How must one imagine Sisyphus?

_____

_____

Page 1056: According to the speaker, what can a person see when glancing backward over his or her life on earth? What does this action help a person to do?

_____

_____

_____

3. **Responding to the Selection, page 1057.** Reread the following quote by Oedipus: "Despite so many ordeals . . . [I] conclude that all is well." What does this mean to you? Can you say this about your own life? Why, or why not?

_____

_____

_____

_____

_____

_____

_____

_____

_____

_____

_____

_____

_____

_____

_____

_____

_____

_____

_____

_____

_____

_____

_____

RESPONDING IN WRITING

1. **Prewriting: Reinventing a Traditional Character, page 1058.** With other
    members of your class, brainstorm a list of characters from myths, folk tales, and fairy
    tales. From this list choose one character about whom you would like to write. In the
    space below, jot down the key elements of the story of your character. Then write
    some original details about what your character thinks or feels.

    _____

    _____

    _____

    _____

    _____

    _____

    _____

    _____

    _____

    _____

    _____

2. **Prewriting: Critical Essay, page 1058.** Answer the following questions to help you
    organize your ideas for your essay.

    What does Camus believe is tragic in the situation of Sisyphus and the average
    working person?

    _____

    _____

    _____

    In what way is the plight of Sisyphus more tragic?

    _____

    _____

    _____

    What is the one thing both Sisyphus and the average working person can do to make
    their lives less tragic?

    _____

    _____

    _____

Selection Worksheet

"Request to a Year," page 1060

READER RESPONSE ACTIVITIES

1. **Reader's Journal, page 1061.** If you were to borrow one talent or character trait from an older relative, friend, or mentor, what would it be? In what way would this talent or character trait help you in your own life?

   _____

   _____

   _____

   _____

2. **Guided Reading.** Answer these questions as you read the selection.

   Page 1061: What gift would the speaker like to have?

   _____

   _____

   Page 1061: What does the speaker's great-great-grandmother view from a difficult distance?

   _____

   _____

   Page 1061: What does the second daughter do to help her brother?

   _____

   _____

   Page 1062: What does the great-great-grandmother do as the incident unfolds?

   _____

   _____

3. **Responding to the Selection, page 1062.** What do you think of the speaker's request? Do you share her feelings of admiration for her great-great grandmother? Why, or why not?

   _____

   _____

   _____

RESPONDING IN WRITING

1. **Prewriting: Tribute, page 1063.** First choose the person you will honor with your tribute. Then do a focused freewrite on each of the following questions: Why is this person admirable? What character traits or actions make this person stand out? What one anecdote would demonstrate this person's character? In response to the last question you might freewrite stories you know about this person and later choose one that is especially telling. Begin freewriting in the space below and continue on your own paper.

_____

_____

_____

_____

_____

_____

_____

_____

_____

_____

_____

2. **Prewriting: Critical Essay, page 1063.** After examining the theme and title of "Request to a Year," organize your ideas for your essay in the outline form below. Use your own paper if you need additional space.

    I. _____

       A. _____

          1. _____

          2. _____

       B. _____

          1. _____

          2. _____

   II. _____

       A. _____

          1. _____

          2. _____

       B. _____

          1. _____

          2. _____

Selection Worksheet

12.8

"The First Sally (A) or Trurl's Electronic Bard," page 1065

READER RESPONSE ACTIVITIES

1. **Reader's Journal, page 1066.** Do you believe that computers can take the place of humans in all areas? Why, or why not? Are you excited by advances in computer technology, or do such advances ever worry or bother you? Explain.

_____

_____

_____

_____

_____

_____

_____

_____

_____

_____

_____

_____

_____

_____

_____

_____

_____

_____

2. **Guided Reading.** Answer these questions as you read the selection.

   Page 1066: What does the narrator say about Trurl's "sally"? Why should it be considered a far journey even though Trurl didn't go anywhere?

   _____

   _____

   _____

Page 1066: What does Trurl decide to build? Why does he decide to build this thing? What books does he read to begin his work?

_____

_____

_____

Page 1066: Why is building a poetry machine so complicated? What does Trurl need to do in order to match what is in the head of the average poet?

_____

_____

_____

Page 1067: Why is Trurl able to repeat historical events at a fast rate? What challenge does the narrator present to the reader?

_____

_____

_____

Page 1067: What happens to the machine at the end of the twentieth century? When does this story take place?

_____

_____

_____

Page 1067: What are the only two problems that occur? Why do they occur?

_____

_____

Page 1068: What electronic devices does Trurl add to the machine? What do these devices do to the machine's personality? What is the machine finally ready to do?

_____

_____

_____

Page 1068: What alterations does Trurl make to the machine? Describe how each of these adjustments affects the machine as a "character."

_____

_____

_____

Page 1068: What does Trurl think of the machine's first poem? What is he forced to install?

_____

_____

_____

Page 1069: What does the machine's voice sound like? What is wrong with the poetry?

_____

_____

_____

Page 1069: What does Trurl find that he believes is causing the problem?

_____

_____

_____

Page 1070: Is Klapaucius impressed with the machine's poetry? What does he say about it?

_____

_____

_____

Page 1070: What kind of poem does Klapaucius ask the machine to compose? What is Trurl's reaction to this request? Is the machine able to do it?

_____

_____

_____

Page 1071: Why does Trurl become annoyed with Klapaucius? What does he want Klapaucius to ask the machine?

_____

_____

_____

Page 1071: What kind of love poem does Klapaucius demand?

_____

_____

_____

Page 1071: Why does Klapaucius leave? How does Trurl explain his departure? What does Klapaucius tell people about Trurl?

_____

_____

_____

Page 1072: Why do the avant-garde poets make fun of Trurl's machine? What is the machine's poetic background?

_____

_____

_____

Page 1072: How do true poets react to the electronic bard?

_____

_____

Page 1072: What do magazine editors and readers like about Trurl's machine?

_____

_____

Page 1072: Why do the third-rate poets remain unaffected by the machine?

_____

_____

Page 1073: What does the machine do from the asteroid? What is Trurl ordered to do?

_____

_____

Page 1073: What happens when Trurl tries to dismantle the machine?

_____

_____

Page 1073: How is the problem of getting rid of the bard finally solved?

_____

_____

Page 1074: What is Trurl's vow?

_____

_____

3. **Responding to the Selection, page 1074.** What do you think of the "electronic bard"? Is it likely that one could really be invented? Why, or why not?

_____

_____

_____

_____

_____

_____

_____

_____

_____

_____

_____

_____

_____

_____

_____

_____

RESPONDING IN WRITING

1. **Prewriting: Science Fiction Description, page 1076.** Begin by freewriting about possible inventions on your own paper. Then, in the space below, gather details about the invention you chose. Freewrite about what your invention looks like and sounds like, how the invention helps people, how you created it, problems you addressed, problems that may still exist, and any other details you can think of related to your invention.

_____

_____

_____

_____

_____

_____

_____

_____

_____

_____

_____

_____

_____

_____

_____

_____

_____

_____

_____

_____

2. **Prewriting: Critical Essay, page 1076.** First identify the elements of the story that make it science fiction. Then identify what Lem satirizes with each element. Use the chart below to organize your ideas.

ELEMENT OF SCIENCE FICTION	SATIRE

Selection Worksheet

from *Being There*, page 1078

READER RESPONSE ACTIVITIES

1. **Reader's Journal, page 1079.** Think about a time when you did not know the answer to a question you were asked or when you did not understand a conversation in which you were expected to take part. How did you handle the situation? Did you ask questions or admit your lack of knowledge? Did you try to pretend that you understood? Did you change the subject or leave the conversation? Write about the conversation, how you participated, and how you felt about the situation.

_____

_____

_____

_____

_____

_____

_____

_____

_____

_____

_____

_____

_____

_____

_____

_____

2. **Guided Reading.** Answer these questions as you read the selection.

Page 1079: What does Rand warn Chance that the Secret Service people will do? What does he tell Chance not to show them? What does Chance make of Rand's remarks?

_____

_____

_____

Page 1079: Who is going to visit Rand? Why is this person making this visit? What does Rand want Chance to do?

_____

_____

Page 1080: How does Chance react to the President's arrival? Is he comfortable in this situation?

_____

_____

Page 1080: Where does Chance remember seeing the President before? What image does Chance have of the President?

_____

_____

Page 1081: What does Chance remember about the President? What does he do as a result of this memory? What might this action suggest to the President about Chance?

_____

_____

_____

Page 1082: What is the President's opinion of Chance's comments? How does the President interpret Chance's remarks?

_____

_____

Page 1082: Why doesn't Chance take part in the conversation? What does he think Rand and the President are doing?

_____

_____

Page 1082: To what are Chance's thoughts compared? What does Chance say when asked about the "bad season on The Street"?

_____

_____

Page 1083: What does Chance do after the President leaves? What does he see? What is his reaction to this sight?

_____

_____

3. **Responding to the Selection, page 1083.** What do you think of Chance? If the president asked for your opinion about making Chance an advisor, what would you say? Write a response for or against giving Chance such a position.

_____

_____

_____

_____

_____

_____

_____

_____

_____

_____

_____

_____

_____

_____

_____

_____

_____

_____

RESPONDING IN WRITING

1. **Prewriting: News Story, 1085.** Think of six questions you might like to ask Chance. Write your questions in the space below. Use your own paper to write additional questions you might like to ask.

Who _____ ?

What _____ ?

When _____ ?

Where _____ ?

How _____ ?

Why _____ ?

2. **Prewriting: Critical Essay, page 1085.** Before drafting your essay, consider the following questions: What can seeing the world through the eyes of simple or naive characters reveal? Why might such characters be used for social criticism? What does the name of each character suggest? What difficulties or misunderstandings occur when the naive character interacts with others? Are Chance and Candide similar or do their experiences differ greatly? You may wish to refer to the story as you answer some of these questions. Begin responding in the space provided.

_____

_____

_____

_____

_____

_____

_____

_____

_____

_____

_____

_____

_____

_____

_____

_____

_____

_____

_____

_____

_____

_____

_____

_____

_____

_____

_____

_____

Selection Worksheet

"Snapshots of a Wedding," page 1086

READER RESPONSE ACTIVITIES

1. **Reader's Journal, page 1087.** Why do people sometimes feel threatened by others whose values and ideas are different from their own? Have you ever witnessed such a clash of values and ideas? Have you ever had a conflict or a discussion with someone whose system of values and ideas was vastly different from yours? Write about this situation on the lines below.

_____

_____

_____

_____

_____

_____

_____

_____

_____

_____

_____

_____

_____

_____

_____

_____

_____

_____

_____

_____

_____

_____

2. **Guided Reading.** Answer these questions as you read the selection.

Page 1087: When do wedding days begin? What do relatives of the bridegroom bring to the bride? Why?

_____

_____

Page 1087: What kind of wedding is taking place? Why is it described in this way?

_____

_____

Page 1088: How does the bride's family feel about the bride? Why do they feel this way? Does Neo know about these feelings?

_____

_____

Page 1088: According to Neo's relatives, why has Kegoletile chosen Neo as his bride?

_____

_____

Page 1088: What secret conflict does Kegoletile experience?

_____

_____

Page 1088: What is the difference between Neo and Mathata?

_____

_____

Page 1089: Why would it be hard to know the true feelings of the family on the day of the wedding?

_____

_____

Page 1089: What does an aunt say to Neo to shock her? What effect do her words have on Neo?

_____

_____

Page 1090: Why is the chopping at the ground with a hoe only a formality?

_____

_____

Page 1090: What does the request for water stand for? What are Neo and Kegoletile told they must do to honor tradition and their marriage vows?

_____

_____

Page 1090: What does the aunt who had scolded Neo say to Neo on the wedding day?

_____

_____

3. **Responding to the Selection, page 1091.** For which character or characters do you feel the most understanding? What qualities does this character possess with which you can identify? Are there any characters whom you are unable to understand? Why?

_____

_____

_____

_____

_____

_____

_____

_____

_____

_____

_____

_____

_____

_____

_____

_____

_____

_____

_____

_____

RESPONDING IN WRITING

1. **Prewriting: Snapshots of an Event, page 1092.** After choosing an event, use the chart below to organize your ideas and to gather vivid details.

POSSIBLE SNAPSHOTS	CHARACTERS INVOLVED	ACTIONS	DIALOGUE

2. **Prewriting: Critical Essay, page 1093.** On your own paper, answer the following questions: What parts of the story show the contrast between the old world and the modern world of which Neo is a part? In what way does the author use the characters of Mathata and Neo to illustrate this contrast? How does the conflict between old and new values affect Kegoletile? Then, in the space below, outline your essay. Continue your outline on your own paper if necessary.

I. _____

   A. _____

      1. _____

      2. _____

   B. _____

      1. _____

      2. _____

II. _____

   A. _____

      1. _____

      2. _____

   B. _____

      1. _____

      2. _____

Selection Worksheet

12.11

"Games at Twilight," page 1094

READER RESPONSE ACTIVITIES

1. **Reader's Journal, page 1095.** Think back to your childhood and describe a time when you felt left out, forgotten, or disillusioned by something. What happened to make you feel this way? How did you feel about being left out or disillusioned? Angry? resentful? frightened? saddened? What did you do about the situation? Write your responses to these questions on the lines below.

_____

_____

_____

_____

_____

_____

_____

_____

_____

_____

_____

_____

_____

_____

2. **Guided Reading.** Answer these questions as you read the selection.

   Page 1095: What is it like outside? In what terms are the animals described?

   _____

   _____

   Page 1095: What do the children want to do? Why do they wish to do this so badly?

   _____

   _____

   Page 1096: What is the "business" of the children? What do they decide to do?

   _____

   _____

Page 1096: What happens when Raghu sees Manu? How would you describe Raghu? To what are the children who hide from him compared?

_____

_____

_____

Page 1096: How do the children decide who will be It? Is there a game you used to play to determine who would be It? If so, describe it.

_____

_____

Page 1097: What two incidents make Ravi wish he were bigger?

_____

_____

Page 1098: To what is the annual cleaning of the shed compared?

_____

_____

Page 1098: Why doesn't Ravi want to enter the shed?

_____

_____

Page 1098: How does Ravi feel once inside the shed? To what is the smell of the shed compared? What similar experience has Ravi had? What makes his current situation different?

_____

_____

_____

Page 1099: What is happening outside the shed?

_____

_____

Page 1099: Why does Ravi "hold out a bit longer"? What does he long to do? What would be so exciting about defeating Raghu?

_____

_____

_____

Page 1099: What has Ravi forgotten?

_____

_____

Page 1100: What does Ravi do as he dashes to the pillar? What makes his voice break? How do the other children react to his appearance?

_____

_____

_____

Page 1100: What have the children been too busy playing to do?

_____

_____

Page 1100: What about Ravi surprises the other children?

_____

_____

Page 1100: What upsets Ravi about the children's new game?

_____

_____

Page 1100: What did Ravi want? What does he get instead? What does he refuse to do?

_____

_____

3. **Responding to the Selection, page 1101.** If you were younger and in Ravi's position, how would you react to his situation? Would you react as he does or in some other way?

_____

_____

_____

_____

_____

_____

_____

_____

RESPONDING IN WRITING

1. **Prewriting: Personal Memoir, page 1102.** Review your responses to the Reader's Journal activity on page 1095. Then fill in the sensory detail chart below with details about the experience you chose.

SENSORY DETAIL CHART				
SIGHT	SOUND	TOUCH	TASTE	SMELL

2. **Prewriting: Critical Essay, page 1102.** On your own paper, do a focused freewrite in response to one of the prewriting prompts on page 1103 of your textbook. Then complete the Venn diagram below.

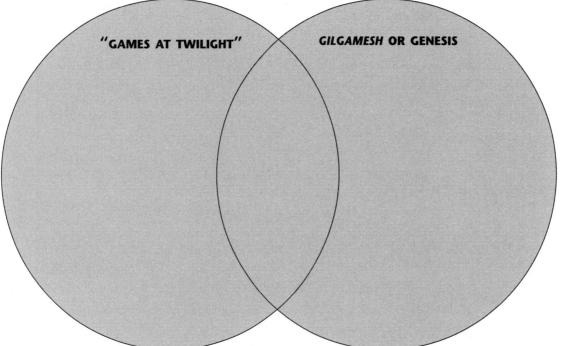

"GAMES AT TWILIGHT"   *GILGAMESH* OR GENESIS

Selection Worksheet

12.12

from *The Woman Warrior,* page 1104

READER RESPONSE ACTIVITIES

1. **Reader's Journal, page 1105.** Do you think your parents and other adults respect you? What expectations do you think they have for your future? Do you share these expectations, or do you have different plans for your future? Write your responses to these questions on the lines below.

_____

_____

_____

_____

_____

_____

_____

_____

_____

_____

_____

_____

_____

_____

_____

_____

2. **Guided Reading.** Answer these questions as you read the selection.

   Page 1105: What did Chinese girls learn from listening to adults talk-story? What does the narrator suppose about the custom of feet-binding?

   _____

   _____

   Page 1105: What power does the narrator come to recognize?

   _____

   _____

Page 1105: What does the narrator hear as a grown-up? What does she remember? What conclusion does she reach?

_____

_____

Page 1106: What is the last battle that the warrior has to fight?

_____

_____

Page 1106: What is the goal of the warrior?

_____

_____

Page 1106: How does the baron treat the warrior? What does he quote? How does the warrior feel about the baron?

_____

_____

Page 1107: Whom does the warrior find when she breaks into the locked room? What happens to these people?

_____

_____

Page 1107: What does the warrior do after finishing her business with the baron?

_____

_____

Page 1107: In what way will the warrior's accomplishments be celebrated?

_____

_____

Page 1108: How does the narrator's mother react to her accomplishments? How does this make the narrator feel?

_____

_____

Page 1108: What good came of the birth of the narrator's brothers? In what way did the birth of her brothers renew the message the narrator had been receiving about girls?

_____

_____

Page 1108: What sayings do the narrator's parents and the other villagers repeat about girls? What is the general attitude toward girls?

_____

_____

Page 1108: What does the "outward tendency in females" mean? What does the narrator intend to prove? How will she prove it?

_____

_____

Page 1109: What does one of the words for the female *I* mean? What does the narrator recognize about language?

_____

_____

Page 1109: Why does the narrator become bitter? In what way has China wrapped double binds on her feet?

_____

_____

3. **Responding to the Selection, page 1109.** At the end of this selection, the narrator says, "Even now China wraps double binds around my feet." Have you been restricted by cultural or societal beliefs or traditions? How do you react to such restrictions?

_____

_____

_____

_____

_____

_____

_____

_____

_____

_____

_____

_____

_____

RESPONDING IN WRITING

1. **Prewriting: Autobiographical Sketch, page 1111.** After choosing an event from your own life as the subject of your sketch, do a focused freewrite for each of the following prompts. Begin in the space provided and continue on your own paper.

   • Where did this event take place? Describe this place in detail.

   • Who else participated in this event? What were their reactions? Write a brief dialogue between the people involved.

   • What sights, sounds, smells, tastes, or objects do you associate with this event?

   • What effect did this event have on you at the time? Why is this event significant to you now?

   _____

   _____

   _____

   _____

   _____

   _____

   _____

   _____

2. **Prewriting: Critical Essay, page 1111.** Fill in the chart below with elements from the works of Kingston and Wright as well as your own opinions. In the first column, identify constraints in *The Woman Warrior* and "Request to a Year"; in the second column, write the symbolic meaning of these constraints; and in the third column, write your own ideas or opinions about these constraints.

CONSTRAINT	SYMBOLIC MEANING	MY OPINION

Selection Worksheet

"The Wooden Horse then said," page 1112

READER RESPONSE ACTIVITIES

1. **Reader's Journal, page 1113.** Think about a time in your life when you asked someone a difficult or controversial question and this person changed the subject to avoid talking about the issue. Why do you think he or she tried to talk about something else? Was it an effective tactic in the short-term? in the long-term? On the lines below, write your opinion of changing the subject to avoid controversy.

_____

_____

_____

_____

_____

_____

_____

_____

_____

_____

_____

_____

_____

_____

_____

_____

_____

2. **Guided Reading.** Answer these questions as you read the selection.

   Page 1113: What does the wooden horse refuse to do?

   _____

   _____

   Page 1113: What does the wooden horse claim?

   _____

   _____

Page 1113: What does the wooden horse say he did in his "younger days"?

_____

_____

3. **Responding to the Selection, page 1114.** Imagine that you are the member of the press who asked the question that prompted the wooden horse's response. What did you ask? What are you trying to discover? How do you feel about the wooden horse's response?

_____

_____

_____

_____

RESPONDING IN WRITING

1. **Prewriting: Poem or Fable with an Unusual Point of View, page 1115.** With other members of your class, brainstorm a list of flaws in the world. Then choose one of these problems as the subject of your poem or fable. On the lines below, freewrite from your chosen point of view about this subject.

_____

_____

_____

_____

_____

_____

_____

2. **Prewriting: Critical Essay, page 1115.** After reviewing the poem and analyzing the tone, make a rough outline of your essay on the lines below. Continue on your own paper as necessary.

_____

_____

_____

_____

_____